Practical Yoga
Psychology

1963–2013
GOLDEN JUBILEE

WORLD YOGA CONVENTION 2013
GANGA DARSHAN, MUNGER, BIHAR, INDIA
23rd–27th October 2013

Practical Yoga Psychology

Dr Rishi Vivekananda

Yoga Publications Trust, Munger, Bihar, India

Published by Yoga Publications Trust
   First edition 2005
   Reprinted 2006, 2008, 2009, 2012

ISBN: 978-81-86336-39-7

Publisher and distributor: Yoga Publications Trust, Ganga Darshan, Munger, Bihar, India.

Website: www.biharyoga.net
          www.rikhiapeeth.net

Printed at Thomson Press (India) Limited, New Delhi, 110001

Dedication

In humility we offer this dedication to
Swami Sivananda Saraswati, who initiated
Swami Satyananda Saraswati into the secrets of yoga.

This book is dedicated to Swami Satyananda Saraswati who made it happen, and Swami Niranjanananda Saraswati who suggested it in the first place.

Contents

x

Introduction

What do people need nowadays? What has happened to our peace of mind? There is an old Chinese curse: "May you live in interesting times." The word 'interesting' means that there is a lot going on, that life is very complicated because of the strife around us. That certainly applies to this era we are going through. There is personal, political and environmental turmoil all around the world, many people have lost their spiritual roots, and our minds can't keep up with the rapid change. Our emotions also are corrupted by the intake of mental impressions, emotional input, unnatural food and drinks, etc., and although nutrition is inadequate in many parts of the world, in the affluent parts the food we are taking into our bodies is far too high in fat, salt, sugar and impurities.

Just when everyone is wondering how we can solve the accelerating human dilemma, the ancient science of yoga is rapidly spreading throughout the world. What is yoga? Can we understand it? Can it explain how we relate to each other? Can it help us to understand each other? What benefits can we expect from it? Can it help us to evolve the qualities of our personality? The answer to all these questions is a definite, "yes".

It is the age-old question: why do other people behave the way they do? Why do I? In some ways we are so similar, in others so different. If we don't know why *we* think, feel

1

and behave in the way we do, we can't understand each other either, and where there is so little understanding, how can there be love between us? So many of the 'misunderstandings' between people, countries, cultural groups, religions, etc., arise because of this ignorance of the differences between us and how they arise. If we can learn to understand ourselves and each other, maybe we will be able to come into harmony with ourselves, other people and the world around us. If we can learn to understand ourselves, we can start to evolve ourselves to become our highest potential. How can we?

Yoga has tackled this question of human personality and its development, and has done it in a unique way. The insights into personality have been developed over thousands of years by people in high states of awareness, intuition and psychic realization. Not surprisingly, some of the answers are very similar to conclusions reached independently by Western observers in recent times. However, some of them are very different and they should be given much more attention in the West.

What are you looking for?

If you are an ordinary person looking for a way to find peace of mind and some meaning in life, this book will explain the yogic view of human life and destiny, and how we can develop our potentials. It will also indicate some simple but effective practices with which to start.

If you want to go on and evolve the very heart of your nature, you will find some of the answers here and suggestions as to how you can proceed further.

If you are a psychiatrist, psychologist, or other health worker in the field, this book will give you a much wider view of the human person and their potentials to integrate with what you already know. It will give you an overview of a comprehensive view of human personality and destiny that is far wider than any even suspected by the Western mind.

Yoga is simple to understand, and the practices are easy to do for the person who is properly prepared.

Making my apologies early
A note on genders
I try to be fair when using genders while talking or writing, but it is always a problem when one uses singular gender pronouns. It is easy with plurals, we just write 'they'; for example, "When people laugh *they* caress *their* immune systems." With singulars it used to be the convention to write the masculine; for example, "When a person laughs *he* caresses *his* immune system," but that is not acceptable because it is gender discrimination. What do we do? One option is to write '*he or she*' or vice versa or alternating them, another is '*he/she*' or vice versa or alternating them, but both these forms are a little clumsy and they slow the reading. I have even seen '*s/he*', but that is really 'she' and that is gender discrimination too. The solution I have adopted in this book is to honour the rules of fairness by breaking a rule of grammar. I use *they, their, them,* etc., for both singular and plural. I know it is incorrect grammar, but it smoothes out the flow of reading, and anyway it is commonly used by even well-educated people when they speak.

There is one exception to this principle though, which is when I am directly quoting from the work of another author. The 'rule' states clearly that as well as giving the name of the author and the source, the quote must be verbatim.

A note on Sanskrit terms
Why have I used Sanskrit words in this book? Couldn't I have stuck to a modern language like English? What is Sanskrit anyway? Sanskrit is the language of ancient India, so the classic texts from which yoga comes were written in this language. Needless to say yoga is replete with Sanskrit terms, but in this book I have used English where it is an equivalent (even a 'rough' one). Frequently where I have used an English equivalent, I have followed it with the Sanskrit term in italics and/or brackets, so that you can easily find it in the recommended texts. If you like, you can just skim over those and leave them till you need them later.

However, there are some words that don't have an equivalent. There are some words that denote concepts and states of consciousness that are not even dreamt of by the non-yogic mind, so there couldn't be equivalent words in English, French, Spanish, Arabic or any other language. I have had to use the Sanskrit word for these. Moreover, even when a Sanskrit word seems to have an equivalent, it often doesn't exactly fit – even using the word 'posture' to denote the physical practice called 'asana' doesn't really describe its full implications. But we do the best we can.

A note on my approach to the subject

I am going to present a very small part of an enormous field that is yoga; a system that has vast ramifications, gross and subtle. To keep this as simple as possible, I have tried to stick to the area of *personality*, and what seemed to me, at the time of writing, to be some of the most relevant yogic concepts that apply to its evolution. If any yoga savants believe that I have not given their favourite areas of yoga due treatment, or that I have approached the whole thing from a peculiar angle, I agree. But maybe, just maybe, it will be of some value.

Where do we go from here?

Let us now look deeper into some of the main principles of yoga, so that we can then put them together to get an overview of a yogic viewpoint of personality and its evolution. We can then understand just how yoga can help each one of us to evolve in this way, and how the practices help us do it.

First of all, in Chapter 1 we will ask, "What is yoga?" and try to solve that problem right at the start. The next five chapters will develop some of the fundamental principles of yoga. Chapter 2, on the koshas, will enlarge our viewpoint to take in the full extent and potential of the human individual. Chapter 3 will introduce the chakra systems, the centres that define the different *aspects of our personality*. Then, in Chapter 4, we will look at the gunas which, among other things, explain the degrees of *evolvement of our personality*. This will take us, in Chapter 5, to the important principle of *balance within us*, and then, in Chapter 6, we will consider the *workings of the human mind* from the yogic point of view, and its areas of agreement with the viewpoint of Western psychology.

Then it will be our task to integrate the principles above to form a clear picture of how they *combine* to create our personality, and explain guidelines as to how we can evolve it. Chapter 7, the first in this integration process, will paint a picture of how the different *aspects of our personality* are represented by the *chakra systems*. Chapter 8 will explain the different levels of *evolvement* of each of those personality aspects as seen through the perspective of the gunas. Chapter 9 will introduce the concept of how an individual's personality is influenced by one or two of those *aspects* being *dominant* within that person. Chapter 10 will combine the above into a *seven-dimensional model of the human personality*.

Chapters 11–15 will suggest beneficial yogic principles we can integrate into our way of life, and this will be followed, in Chapters 16 and 17, by a practical outline of many of the techniques that augment our yogic lifestyle to evolve our personality. Then, finally, in Chapters 18 and 19, we will integrate the above principles into a whole picture of how yoga evolves all the aspects of our personality.

Some Principles
of Yoga

1

What is Yoga?

Everybody knows what yoga is, don't they? That stuff the movie stars are doing nowadays to keep themselves thin? Maybe, but it's not what they call it that's important; it's what they are actually doing that tells us whether it is yoga or not.

Physical jerks at the gym? The more they are smooth and easy, the more they may approach true yoga practices. But many are just aerobic series using yoga postures as their form, and because of their quick extreme stretching with bouncing 'ballistic' movements they are not yoga.

"No pain, no gain." This may be a fundamental rule of the sport of masochism, but it has no place in yoga.

Tying up like a pretzel is often the image people have of the postures, but actually the ideal postures are those simple, relaxing stretches suited to the experience of the ordinary person.

Corporate stress release? Yoga has been proved to be a beneficial stress-relieving system, and can be used by anyone right in the middle of a stressful situation – close but only a small part of it.

The classes at the local yoga school, of which there are tens of thousands throughout the world? Yes, getting there. Insofar as they are taught by experienced yoga teachers who have 'been there' themselves, using simple techniques suited to the fitness, flexibility and experience of the student, they may certainly approach a small amount of what we try to accomplish from yoga.

The yogi in deep meditation in a cave is also an image people have. However, most yogis are deeply involved in the world for the benefit of the world and the people in it and certainly have little time for sitting in caves.

People have many ideas of what yoga is, but rarely do they come anywhere near the width and depth of yoga. The object of this book is to paint a picture of the extent of yoga, and to explain how we can use it in our lives to realize our highest potentials.

DEFINITIONS OF YOGA

It has been said that if you want to put an audience to sleep, start with a definition. Maybe a reader will doze off if an author does the same. However, in order to understand the presentation in this book, we will have to agree on what we are talking about when we use such words as 'yoga', 'personality' etc.

There are many definitions of yoga, mainly depending on the direction from which we look at it. Here are three of these perspectives.

1. What are we trying to accomplish in life, and how can yoga help?
2. What is the mechanism through which yoga works?
3. What practices can we use to accomplish this?

We will deal with these in order now, remembering that they are all part of a continuous whole, and we are just looking at yoga from different directions.

What are we trying to accomplish in life, and how can yoga help?

This brings us to our first definition of yoga, which is very clear about this – it says that we are trying to EVOLVE all of our different dimensions as individuals. A definition from this perspective could be the following one, derived from a definition given by Swami Niranjan:

Yoga is an ancient system of philosophy, lifestyle and techniques that *evolves the whole person*, the physical, the vitality, the mind and emotions, wisdom, ethics and a higher quality of relationships, and the realization of the spiritual reality of each of us.

He adds:

According to the yogic tradition, evolution is a systematic process through which we learn to harmonize ourselves. It is a process through which we develop the ability to express our qualities optimally and creatively.

There are many important points here. Let's take them one by one.

1. Yoga is ancient – the very early beginnings

As yoga is a system of personal inquiry and experience, one might say that it began when humans first became aware and started asking questions of self-discovery. Animals can 'know' something, but do they *'know* that they know'? Humans do have this kind of awareness, and it formed the substrata of our thirst for self-discovery. Knowledge of the body and its functions was the beginning of self-understanding, knowledge of the mind and its processes was the beginning of self-awareness, and experience of the transcendental force/spirit was the beginning of self-realization.

These required a healthy and vital body, so they developed the yoga postures, cleansing practices and breathing practices. They needed clarity of mind, so they developed systems of concentration and mental clarity, which became the meditation practices. With the agricultural revolution, as they started to live in more concentrated communities, they evolved philosophies and behaviour that developed harmony between themselves.

As people observed the different manifestations of nature, they started asking questions about destiny, the creator, the meaning of life and the person's place in it. The word 'yoga' comes from the Sanskrit *yug*, which means 'yoke', which itself indicates a joining together, a unity, a harmony, balance between internal and external consciousness and manifestation. So yoga means self-knowledge, understanding, awareness, and union with the highest consciousness as the ultimate development.

The earliest written evidence of what we would call 'yoga' dates back more than 4,000 years to the early Vedas. There is evidence of it having been more widespread throughout the world, but due to the vagaries of politics, war and famine, the major place where it carried on was in the area we now call India. It is from here that it is now spreading rapidly all over the world. It is believed that even prior to the written forms, it was propagated down the generations by word of mouth from teacher to student. Even after it was written down, the oral transmission continued, and still continues, especially for the more powerful 'secret' practices.

2. Philosophy

The philosophical underpinnings of yoga are vast, and embrace many ancient systems such as Samkhya, Vedanta and Tantra. They of course deal with one's personal reality, one's place in the family, society, planet Earth and the universe itself.

Yoga philosophy attempts to give meaning to our beliefs about such fundamentals as *ourselves* – what are we all about? *Purpose* – is there a purpose to our being here, does life have a meaning or do we just appear then disappear like a wave on the water? *Health, wellbeing, illness, pain* – do these have any meaning, are they just luck, or are they in our lives to teach us something? And finally *death* – is there anything after it, and did it really have any meaning in the end?

Yoga also considers our relationships with *other people* – the basics of their nature; with our personal place in *society*

12

– our duties and privileges; and with *divinity* – whether the ultimate consciousness exists, and if it does, what role it has in the formation of 'all this' and its continuance.

However, it is important to note that although yoga has an extensive philosophical background, we are not instructed to believe it, and this is one of the ways that yoga is certainly not a religion. Yoga is not a belief system, although it has branches such as bhakti yoga for people who already believe; it is really about our personal experience. We are encouraged to hold the philosophy as only possibilities, practise the techniques and lifestyle principles, and move along the good path, just because it is good and beneficial. Then as we evolve in our own right, we will become increasingly aware of the reality and our personal place in it.

3. Lifestyle principles

We will deal with lifestyle in much greater detail later. Let us just say at this point that yoga is crucially concerned with how we live our life with respect to: (i) our own personal health, hygiene and wellbeing, (ii) our personal environment, (iii) how we interact with other people, (iv) how we work and behave in general, (v) our life as a learning process and (vi) our relationship with the ultimate consciousness, if we perceive that to be of importance at this stage of our development.

4. Yoga techniques

Yoga is a vast treasure house of techniques that have a beneficial effect on the body, the vitality, the mind, emotions, our intellectual and feeling states, and that lead to the uncovering of our latent potentials. We will also deal with this area in much more detail – theory and practice – later.

But why do we bother to try to change? Why do we do all this? Why are we interested in yoga in the first place? Because of the next word in the definition: *'evolves'*. This is the crux of the whole thing.

5. Evolvement

Evolvement is the key word in the whole book, and its theme. According to yoga, evolvement is the key concept in the whole of one's life. It is the process that allows everything else to happen. It presents us with the realization that each human being is capable – in just this lifetime – of progressing far past their present level of thinking, feeling and functioning. Yoga is really all about how we can evolve ourselves this way.

What is it that we 'evolve'? We are told this in the rest of the definition, which outlines some of the characteristics of 'the whole person'. We are introduced to the holistic view of the human individual presented to us by yoga. It deals with the five sheaths *(koshas)* of the person: the physical body, the vitality body, the mental body, the wisdom body and the bliss body, which leads us to the realization of the spiritual reality of each one of us. We will discuss these in detail in later sections.

But remember that Swami Niranjan added two more important points to the definition – *harmonizing ourselves* and *expressing our qualities*.

6. We learn to harmonize ourselves

The harmony we develop through yoga occurs on many planes of our being. Remember we said that the word 'yoga' comes from the Sanskrit *yug*, meaning, 'yoke', which indicates a joining together, a unity, a harmony, balance.

This is just what yoga does. For a start, it harmonizes the relationship between the five sheaths, also improving any that are ailing, such as a sick body, low/unbalanced vitality, or disturbed mind and emotions. It also harmonizes the parts within those sheaths; for instance, the physical practices harmonize the endocrine, neurological and immune systems, the meditation practices harmonize our perceptions, thinking, emotions and behaviour, etc.

Ultimately, of course, according to the teachings of yoga, the result is harmony and unity of the person's individual consciousness with the ultimate consciousness.

7. We develop the ability to express our qualities optimally and creatively

Is this what it is all about? We develop to our highest potential so that we can express ourselves in the world in the most efficient and creative way? According to Swami Niranjan, it's a good start. Maybe the primary object of the whole exercise of self-evolution is to make us mightily capable of taking our place in the service of planet Earth and all the beings on it. It's a bit disappointing for those people who were looking forward to retiring after enlightenment and floating off into nirvana. There's an old Buddhist saying: "Before enlightenment, chopping wood and carrying water; after enlightenment, chopping wood and carrying water," but it's a chopping and carrying from a very different level of consciousness. What a contribution we could make to the world then! And remember that on the way there, as we improve, our joy, love, peace of mind, creativity and quality of expression improve apace. So if that idea appeals to you, let's develop it and see where it takes us.

What is the mechanism through which yoga works?

Over 2,500 years ago, the great Sage Patanjali wrote one of the greatest ancient treatises of all time on the human condition. An 'instruction manual' on meditation, the *Yoga Sutras* clearly explains the mechanism by which we human beings can evolve to our highest potential. However, he wrote it in a very succinct style, in short statements in the Sanskrit language, so in its original form its teachings are not available to many people.

Fortunately, over the centuries enlightened sages have written some easily understandable commentaries on the sutras, and one of the latest and easiest to understand is *Four Chapters on Freedom* by Swami Satyananda. This makes clear the beautiful thinking quality of this great master who obviously experienced the exalted states of consciousness of which he wrote.

15

Right at the beginning of the *Yoga Sutras*, Sage Patanjali tells us that yoga is finding peace of mind, but he means a much deeper level of 'mind' than most of us would imagine. His concise definition of yoga is:

Yogaschitta vritti nirodhah
To block the patterns of consciousness is yoga.

Swami Satyananda tells us: *"Chitta* means 'individual consciousness'." This is the whole consciousness of the person. It is the combination of the person's conscious day-to-day mind, plus all the deep memories, including the repressed material, plus all the subtle dimensions of the expanded mind (sometimes called 'super-conscious').

He goes on to say: "The expression *nirodhah* in the sutra apparently means a process of blocking, but it should not mean an act of blocking the fundamental stuff of awareness. In fact, it is clear in this sutra that it is an act of blocking the *patterns* (or disturbances) of awareness, not the awareness itself."

Now this is a very big task; this level of peace of mind is a high one indeed. Those of us who have done some meditation practice will have experienced the peace we felt in bypassing our ordinary conscious thought patterns. We will have even experienced the long term benefits of rooting out the undesirable repressed material in our deep memory which has been causing disturbance in our mind. But to subdue the ripples of disturbance throughout our whole individual consciousness . . .

Talking about these high states of realization which are experienced by the few realized individuals in the world is all very well, but what about us? What about the ordinary people who are still battling with resentments, worries, jealousies, revenge, bigotry, etc.? The fortunate thing is that the blockages that hold us back from realizing our highest potentials are the same ones that are causing our day-to-day conflicts and problems. So the meditation practices are just as useful to improve our everyday experiences and relationships as they are to ultimately lead us to the highest states of consciousness.

So it is from this viewpoint that we will be observing what Sage Patanjali has to say to us.

Five patterns of consciousness

We have established that we have to *block* the *patterns* within our *individual consciousness*, but what are these *vrittis* or patterns? Sage Patanjali lists them in sutra 6 as:

> *Pramana viparyaya vikalpa nidra smritayuh.*
> The fivefold modifications of mind are right knowledge, wrong knowledge, fancy, sleep and memory.

This may sound a little obscure, but if we look at it simply, we will see that Sage Patanjali is describing exactly the same areas in which modern psychology and psychiatry work, though they do so only at the level of the day-to-day conscious mind and the memories, not the whole individual consciousness. Still, we can start here.

1. *Right knowledge*: The things that we know that are true. Many of our problems are caused by overvaluing and overinterpreting, or giving too much weight, either positive or negative, to the realities in our life. And the more negatively we think about them and the more we feel unable to cope with them, the more distressing they are. A lot of my time as a psychiatrist was spent encouraging people to find solutions to the real problems of their life that they thought they could not handle, and to help them accept and give less importance to the ones that can't be solved. Many people spend a lot of time building small stuff into a big deal. Yoga allows us to get a real perspective on these 'realities', and to treat them for what they really are.

2. *Wrong knowledge*: The things we think we know, but that are not true. The whole area of cognitive psychotherapy deals with people's unrealistic beliefs about themselves, about other people and about the world around them. Our perceptions of our world and the people in it, our thinking patterns, our opinions and attitudes, and our habitual responses can all be wrong.

Aaron Beck spoke about what he called 'cognitive distortions' – the way people make themselves ill emotionally and mentally by being preoccupied with wrong 'knowledge'. He described how people can make themselves depressed by generalizing, personalizing, magnifying, minimizing, trivializing and misinterpreting their own strengths, weaknesses, actions and accomplishments, and those of the people around them.

3. *Fancy*: Problems with fantasizing, worries about things that don't exist, or futures that won't come, or guilt over past actions long gone. Or wasting one's time fantasizing about positive things – wishes – that we are not attaining, mainly because we are spending too much time in fantasy.

4. *Sleep*: Even when we are asleep, the processes of the mind can cause disturbances in the field of our mind. The yogis who experience high states of consciousness tell us they are 'awake' even in 'deep sleep', but most of us are not aware of this. However, we know that disturbance can certainly occur in dreams. How many people are constantly 'haunted' by recurring nightmares when they are trying to get sound restful sleep? In my psychiatric practice I used to see a lot of war veterans with post-traumatic stress disorder. Many had terrible flashback experiences of the war in dreams at night. Some had been having regular nightmares about being shot at by enemy soldiers for over 60 years since World War II.

5. *Memory*: The unconscious mind is a potent source of disturbance – mental, emotional, physical etc. This has been known in the West for over a hundred years and in yoga for thousands of years. Many emotionally-loaded memories and desires are repressed deep in the mind, and they cause disturbance at all levels of our being. The long term way of dealing with these, whether by meditation or psychotherapy, is to bring them up into the awareness when one is in a neutral balanced state of mind, and thus neutralize them by stripping them of their 'charge' of painful emotion.

Where are we going from here? And how do we get there? The path we are considering here is yoga. Sage Patanjali

gives the answer simply in what are now known as the eight limbs of raja yoga:
1. Self-restraints and ethics – the quality of our relationships *(yamas)*
2. Personal codes for self-improvement *(niyamas)*
3. Meditation postures *(asanas)*
4. Breath control practices *(pranayamas)*
5. Mental withdrawal from outside stimuli – 'going inside' *(pratyahara)*
6. Concentration *(dharana)*
7. Meditation – total concentration *(dhyana)*
8. Transcendental consciousness *(samadhi)*.

Of course, since the time of Sage Patanjali the yoga 'tools' available have expanded greatly and now form a large repertoire, but the principles remain.

Sage Patanjali clearly described the ways we can deal with the human mind: by observing the way we live our personal life, the quality of our relationships with other people, physical techniques we can do, and the meditation practices that first of all eliminate disturbances of consciousness, and ultimately lead us to realize our highest potential.

What practices can we use to accomplish this?
If we ask the average person to tell us what yoga is, they will probably start by describing their idea of the practices of yoga. They may not even think of the perspectives discussed above, which is fair enough, because most people see yoga in terms of the techniques performed, especially the physical ones. Many people don't even realize that meditation practices are a very important part of yoga – they form the heart of it – or that meditation in yoga preceded and gave rise to the other commonly known meditation schools such as Buddhist meditation, Zen and others.

So what practices are available to us in yoga? There is a vast number, so we will only be able to mention a small number of the most commonly used ones here. Firstly, we can divide them into two main groups according to whether we actually perform them, such as the postures and the meditation practices, or whether they form a part of our ongoing lifestyle. This division is not as clear-cut as it seems, because when we get deeper into yoga we realize that there is a lot of overlap between the two. However, for our purposes at this point it can be a handy division.

We will mention the practices briefly here because we will deal with them in more detail later.

Performed practices

Postures (asanas): These are the usual movements and holding positions people associate with yoga, and there are thousands of them. Some are very simple; in fact, the introductory stretching postures we teach beginners in Satyananda Yoga are so easy that even sick people or very old people can do them and get great benefit. Ordinary students do them first to develop the flexibility to do the major postures correctly later.

Cleansing practices (shatkarmas): This is a series of six body cleansing practices that are recommended for people who have various illnesses and also for aspirants who are beginning advanced practices.

Breath practices (pranayamas): These have many functions, such as raising our vitality, relaxation and balancing our various aspects.

Attitudes and locks (mudras and bandhas): These are postural attitudes and muscle locks that have various effects.

Mantra yoga: These are special vibrational sounds that have an effect on all dimensions of the individual. Probably the best known is AUM.

Mental relaxation (pratyahara): These practices allow us to 'retreat inside' from the hurly burly of the world, and find peace within. They are also preliminary to the further stages of meditation.

Meditation (dharana, dhyana and samadhi): These are increasingly deep stages of consciousness, right up to samadhi – the transcendental state. Most people are nowhere

20

near attaining that, but the practices 'on the way' are all good for us at our own level of development.

Lifestyle practices

General lifestyle: Considerations such as simplicity in our life, efficiency, regularity, moderation, activity, and monitoring our physical intake such as foods, drinks, air and drugs. We also watch the quality of our mental and emotional intake, especially from the people in our life, the media, etc.

Raja yoga: Sage Patanjali was very specific about the positive effect on our peace of mind from good ethical relationships with others, and caring for our own wellbeing. He enumerated these in the first two limbs of raja yoga, the *yamas* and the *niyamas*.

Karma yoga: This is a lifestyle principle which very much needs to be understood in the West. It is the way of living and working for others and the world, with detachment from personal expectations and the fruits of our efforts, with maximum awareness, concentration and absorption in the task at hand.

Bhakti yoga: The yoga of devotion, the process of expressing our emotions in a flow of devotion to the divine and in service to others.

Jnana yoga: The yoga of evolution of our knowledge and expansion of our realization about the fundamental realities and meanings of the highest consciousness.

Yoga for the whole person

This has been a short introduction to yoga to try to get a glimpse of the extent of this great system. Yoga is certainly extensive and has a large number of ways to help us evolve ourselves, so there really is a way that suits each of us. Of course, although we can just take a few practices or principles and apply them to our individual lives, the yogis recommend that we use a blended combination of many parts of the system, and gain the extra benefits.

21

Swami Satyananda Saraswati said in *Meditations from the Tantras*:

All forms of yoga aim at bringing about the state of meditation. One type of yoga should not be practised to the exclusion of all others. Though they are usually regarded as the different paths of yoga, a more realistic description would be to call yoga the path, and its different forms the different lanes of that path. This can be compared to a piece of rope composed of various smaller strands. The different strands have separate identities, yet together they form the rope. In the same way the different strands of each type of yoga, when performed in conjunction with each other, form the composite/whole which takes one to meditation.

2

The Koshas – Our Great Human Heritage

The yogic viewpoint of the human being is extensive and exalted. It teaches us that at our centre is the spark of divinity – our spiritual reality – the *atman*. According to the yogic view, a person is a spiritual entity, interacting in the material world, using a body/mind as a vehicle.

The body/mind is equipped with:

- An energy supply (*prana*)
- A sensory/perceptual system to detect activities in the physical world (*jnanendriyas*)
- A sense of 'I'-ness (*ahamkara*)
- Memory (*chitta*)
- A cognitive (thinking, planning) mechanism to assess input and to decide on behaviour (*manas, buddhi and higher*)
- An affective (emotions and feelings – motivational) mechanism to activate behaviour (*manas and higher*)
- Organs of action to approach or avoid the outside objects and otherwise act in the world (*karmendriyas*).

Remember though that the level of evolvement of the mind aspect may be anywhere from the crudity of the animal to the enlightened wisdom of a realized being. Similarly, the affective aspect may be anywhere from apathy and hate to the bliss and all-encompassing love of the highest consciousness.

Clearly, what we have here is a description of the human entity as being an autonomous spiritual consciousness, independent of the body, but using the body/mind complex as a means of interacting in the world, and evolving as a result. According to yoga we are not just smart animals. Eknath Easwaran says in *The Compassionate Universe*:

> Whatever we feel we know about animals – and I suspect there is a good deal still to be learnt – no observation about animal behaviour need hold true for a human being. In me, in you – in every human being – burns a spark of pure compassion; not physical or even mental, but deeply spiritual. Our bodies may belong to the animal world, but we do not. The animal to a great extent lives subject to the force of (instinct and) conditioning, going after its own food and comfort. But we have the capacity to turn our back on profit or pleasure, for the sake of others – to rebel deeply and broadly against our conditioning and to build a new personality, a new world. It is our choice whether to exercise that capacity, but we do have the choice.[1]

The idea of the individual consciousness being independent of the body is a far cry from the Western concept. The Western scientific viewpoint is that the body is the primary entity, which produces the consciousness with its brain – the implication being that when the body dies, and with it the brain, consciousness disappears. The yogic viewpoint, based on the realizations of sages over the millennia, is that because the individual consciousness is part of the supreme consciousness, each of us is indestructible and continuous.

THE SHEATHS OF HUMAN EXISTENCE:
THE FIVE KOSHAS

(Please note that some parts of this section may be difficult for beginners to understand. If you have trouble, just get what you can from it and go on. It will become clearer as you develop your knowledge with the rest of the book.)

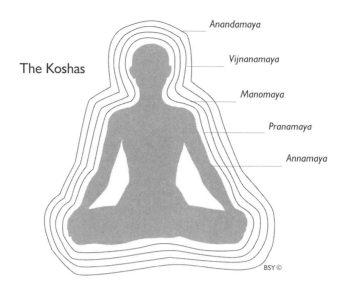

The Koshas

Anandamaya

Vijnanamaya

Manomaya

Pranamaya

Annamaya

BSY©

From the yogic point of view, the body/energy/mind complex is divided into five parts, the grossest being the physical body, the next being the energy body, the next the mental body, then the wisdom body and finally at the finest level, the bliss body. Each of these five is known as a *kosha*, which in Sanskrit means 'sheath'.

So what are the koshas? They are 'the sheaths or dimensions of human existence'.

Each of the five sheaths overlays, covers and obscures the more subtle awareness that is interior to it. So 'sheath' is a good word for these entities because the finer koshas are covered in turn by the next, like sheaths cover the objects inside them. The five levels span the whole spectrum of human nature and provide a model for human evolvement.

The five koshas are:
· Physical body – Annamaya kosha
· Energy body – Pranamaya kosha
· Mental body – Manomaya kosha
· Wisdom body – Vijnanamaya kosha
· Bliss body – Anandamaya kosha
They surround the divine spirit of each of us – the *atman*.

PHYSICAL BODY – Annamaya Kosha (anna = food)

The food body reminds us that we physically become what we eat, so pay attention to what you eat. It is very important to keep the body in optimum health if we are to progress on this path.

The body is the material sheath of our existence. As it is the physical vehicle through which we interact with the created universe, we care for it and nurture it so that it helps to give us joy in life and allows us to go to higher levels without interrupting our progress.

The main practices that work with the physical body are the yoga postures *(asanas)*. With asanas we gain flexibility, relaxation, toning, strength, balance, stress relief and general fitness. The asanas also affect the other koshas, especially pranamaya kosha, balancing the energy, increasing it and removing energy blockages.

In fact, it is a basic truth of yoga that anything that has an influence (positive or negative) on any one of the koshas filters through to affect all the others. All these sheaths are so interrelated that they virtually form the one entity. This means that practices which benefit the other koshas will also help the physical body, and we can experience this from the way we feel physically after doing energizing pranayamas or the relaxation of meditation practices.

ENERGY BODY – Pranamaya Kosha (prana = energy)

Prana is the vital force permeating the body and all of matter. It actually energizes all our koshas, and is *vital for life* at all levels. However, there is energy specific to pranamaya kosha. Yoga views the energy body differently from the Western viewpoint. The science of physiology considers that the energy produced in the cells of the body from the 'burning' of glucose is the only energy source available. The yogis acknowledge that is a source, but claim that the body/energy/mind vehicle obtains its energy from other sources, including the breath, food, water and even directly from the energy of the universe. As with all these levels of prana, pranamaya kosha is a part of the vast energy of the universe (*maha prana*).

The yogis view the energy body as a discrete entity in its own right, which takes up the same space as the physical body but overlaps it. The energy is said to flow through energy channels called *nadis*. A nadi is not a nerve; it is a distinct flow of prana independent of the presence of physical structures. There are similarities between the nadis and the meridians of acupuncture, but it is difficult to compare them directly. There are said to be 72,000 nadis, but estimates vary and it is hard to know who originally counted them!

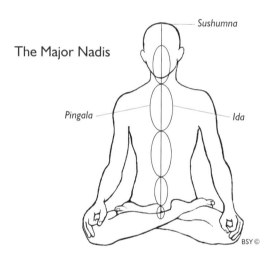

The Major Nadis

Ida, pingala and sushumna

The three most prominent nadis are represented as occurring along the spinal axis, the main central nadi being sushumna, and those running either side of it, ida and pingala. Sushumna is said to represent balance, and ida and pingala the 'moon' and 'sun' aspects of the nature as follows:

Ida: mental force, associated with mental activity, creativity, introversion, feminine, lunar force, the colour blue – right side of the brain, left nostril.

27

Pingala: physical activity, solar energy, extroversion, masculine, the colour red – left brain, right nostril.

Sushumna: becomes active when ida and pingala are balanced, and that time is suitable for meditation. When it is active, a flow of energy known as 'kundalini' is able to rise through it.

Sushumna runs along the axis of the spinal column, and ida and pingala are represented as twining around it on opposite sides, crossing at six points up the length of the spine. Many yoga practices aim at balancing the amount of air flowing through the left and right nostrils, and in turn the flows of ida and pingala nadis (more of this when we discuss swara yoga).

The chakras

At the six points along the sushumna axis where ida and pingala cross are the chakras. The word *chakra* means 'wheel' or 'vortex'. The six major chakras are psychic centres in the subtle body, and are represented in all the koshas – the physical body, energy body, mental body, wisdom body and bliss body. In the energy body *(pranamaya kosha)* they are said to be junction boxes distributing energy throughout the body. The chakras are fundamental to our whole discussion, and we will deal with them in detail in the next chapter, then throughout the book.

The five pranas

According to the teachings of yoga, in some areas the prana serves different functions and is given different names: udana, prana, samana, apana, vyana. With the yoga practices these five are balanced and optimized to maintain good health throughout. The physical areas they serve are:
· Udana – head, arms and legs
· Prana – chest
· Samana – upper abdomen
· Apana – lower abdomen and pelvis
· Vyana – whole body, reserve supply to 'top up' the others.

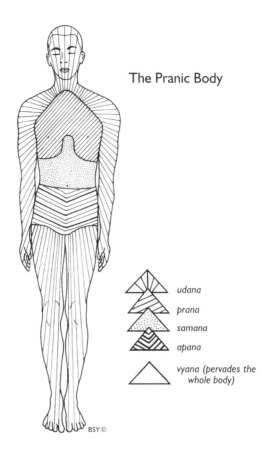

The Pranic Body

udana
prana
samana
apana
vyana (pervades the
whole body)

BSY©

MENTAL BODY – *Manomaya Kosha (mana = mind)*

We will deal with this dimension in much more detail later, but, in brief, manomaya kosha is the mental level that tries to take care of the basic instinctive needs and desires of the individual. These needs are: protection from danger, obtaining food, finding a mate and nurturing the offspring. It acts in response to the input of our senses (sight, hearing, smell, taste and touch), which are constantly monitoring the outside world to give us indications of any events that may be of interest for our safety, food availability, sex, or danger to the young ones.

So the mechanisms of this mental body act at quite a basic level, equivalent to the instinctual mind of the animal, but in addition the process is amenable to being modified by the higher levels of the human mind, so that better decisions can be made, better feeling responses can be experienced and better quality behaviour can result.

The mental body consists of four parts which consistently interact with each other and really do form an efficient team to do the job required. They are:

1. The instinctive mind (manas)
2. The sense of 'I'-ness (ahamkara)
3. Memory (chitta)
4. The lower levels of the intellectual mind (buddhi).

1. *Instinctive mind (manas)*. Its job is to make sense of the world as we experience it. It responds to our perceptions of the sensory input and comes to conclusions such as "What is it?" "Is it good or bad for me?" "Will it hurt me?" "Is it a meal?" "Is it a potential mate?" If left to its own resources, and if it thinks that it should respond to 'that out there', it will usually motivate one of what I call the '3F' responses – fight, flight or friendship.

2. *Sense of 'I'-ness (ahamkara)*. Obviously, if we are to protect ourselves from or benefit from the outside world, we must have a sense of self that sets us apart from it. We must be ever mindful of the 'me' as separate from 'that'. This is the sense of 'I'-ness that the yogis call *ahamkara*.

3. *Memory (chitta)*. Imagine an animal in the jungle – the eyes detect something moving that is separate from 'me'. Manas wants to know "What is it?" It immediately 'asks' the memory, "Have I seen one of these before?" According to the reply, the mind may decide to run away, or try to catch it and eat it, or go over and make friends with it. This is the role of memory at this level. Memory is the storehouse of our past encounters and the experiences we have had with them. This information is crucial to help us decide what to do in 'this' encounter.

4. *The intellectual mind (buddhi)*. At this basic level of functioning, buddhi lends an intellectual mode of helping

manas to reach better decisions for our interactions with the world. Actually, buddhi is in action at much higher levels of mind, right up to the unerring wisdom of the bliss body *(anandamaya kosha)*. But here we see buddhi at its lower levels of rational thinking in the service of manas – far below its exalted abilities, but very valuable in handling our day-to-day activities.

So far we have looked at the physical, vital and thinking responses of the person functioning together, but as humans we are capable of much higher functioning indeed. Of course, there are some people who, for one reason or another, customarily just function at the 'clever animal' (and often not so clever) level. But according to the yogis, even they are basically spirit, and are existing in body/energy/mind 'vehicles' of the highest qualities and potentials.

What are these higher 'koshas' and how do we evolve to function at those levels?

WISDOM BODY – *Vijnanamaya Kosha (vijnana = knowing)*

This is the level of higher buddhi – good intellect, intuition, wisdom, higher knowledge and psychic abilities shining out from anandamaya. At the level of vijnanamaya we experience the higher chitta where most of the dross is cleared out of the unconscious mind, and ahamkara at this level is a sense of 'I'-ness that is part of the 'one'-ness which is us. Our feelings are no longer the crude emotions of survival and exploitation, but the evolved levels of love, compassion, joy, security, accomplishment and mutually fulfilling relationships.

With yoga we increasingly access and develop vijnana-maya by working on the lower three koshas to eliminate the ways we are blocked by them and to reduce our identification with them. But we can also work directly on this higher mind; we can exercise it and give it plenty of good activities to do (boredom switches on the internal monologue of the lower mind, and creates mischief). We can explore new avenues, new philosophies, learn more, pursue all of the areas of yoga. We can mix with people who are functioning at the higher mind level, thinkers, non-egotists, joyous people, karma yogis, loving people. We can work hard, accomplish good things and keep on reaching higher. We can feel vijnanamaya open up, feel it develop bigger and bigger pictures of what life is all about.

Self-actualized people

It is interesting to note that the Western psychotherapies aim for a person to develop to about the level of middle vijnanamaya. We consider such people to be quite special, and we don't even dream of the experience and functioning of the great yogi masters who are at the pinnacle of human development. Abraham Maslow described a group of people who he considered were functioning above the average, and who in yoga we would identify as functioning at the middle wisdom mind (*vijnanamaya*) level. He called them self-actualized people, and after interviewing many of them gave the following characteristics:

1. *Objective* – they perceive life and reality objectively, just as it is, and are able to tolerate uncertainty.
2. *Accepting* – they accept themselves and others as they are.
3. *Honest, simple, humorous* – they are natural, honest, spontaneous and simple in thought and behaviour, and have a good sense of humour.
4. *Work for others* – they are committed to meaningful work, usually for the benefit of others, in which they are problem-centred rather than self-centred.
5. *Independent* – they are independent and value their autonomy and privacy.
6. *Relationships* – they establish deep, satisfying inter-personal relationships with a few compatible people.
7. *Human welfare* – but they have affection for and em-pathy with all humanity, and are concerned for their welfare.

8. *Resist enculturation* – they are resistant to conformity and enculturation, although they are not purposely unconventional.
9. *Creative* – they are highly creative and original in thought.
10. *Democratic* – they are democratic in their outlook and value the rights of other people.

Most people would be very grateful to be functioning at this level, and indeed this is the style of person we see as they pass through the middle levels of their yoga development. The egotism is dissolving away, they are thinking clearly and wisely, their regard and compassion for other people is blossoming, they are coming in touch with their inner joy and humour and they feel a deep personal strength in the face of the challenges of the world. But it is only a part of the way along the path. As we move together through this book it will become clear to us what lies ahead in this beautiful journey of yoga.

BLISS BODY – Anandamaya Kosha (ananda = bliss)

This is the kosha that is in most intimate contact with pure spirit – the atman – the emanation from the divine. The bliss that is ananda is not just an emotion; it is the ineffable experience of peace, love and ecstasy from being in contact with the ultimate consciousness.

What can we say about this level of human experience? There are no words for it. How can we at our present level of functioning imagine the oneness with the absolute, the total security, the transcendental bliss, the vast power for good, the cosmic love, the omniscience, and the total communication with the universal spirit that the person in this state is experiencing?

But the yogis who are at that level tell us that it is the true reality of all of us and, in fact, that we are already at that level! That each one of us already is the highest level of consciousness – we are already pure spirit. However, we are caught down in a lower level of awareness; we are so distracted by all the 'dramas' of our lives that we don't realize who we are.

We need to transcend the 'dramas', then we come home to our true heritage.

CONCENTRATION AT WHICH LEVEL?

The different sheaths – physical body, energy body, mind body, wisdom body and bliss body – give us an overall perspective of the human individual, the vast potential of each of us, and the *similarities* that we share right up to the highest level of consciousness.

However, it can explain some of the *differences* between us also, because most of us have a preponderance of our awareness concentrated in one of these. One question we can ask ourselves is: in which one of these five sheaths do I have my main identification – my concentration – my main point of ongoing awareness? In other words, where do I 'live' in this?

For instance, some people are very *body* conscious; they identify strongly with their bodies; they may feel they are their bodies. Obviously, if I identify in this way with the body, my life will be very much caught up in the body's physical demands, desires, drives etc. Moreover, as the body deteriorates with age, my sense of identity will deteriorate with it, causing a crisis in my life.

Some people are concentrated in sustaining and experiencing their *vitality*, and some identify themselves as being that vitality. If I identify with vitality, then my life will be one of energized activity and a virtual worship of the dynamic side of my nature.

Others are immersed in their *lower mind*; most of their attention is concentrated on identifying things, deciding their relevance, comparing, assessing, judging and making ordinary decisions about everything that is going on around them. And when not much is going on, they ruminate about possibilities in the present, re-experience the past, and

34

anticipate the future. If I identify with manas in this way, my life will be caught up in the ceaseless internal monologue and the emotions that go with it.

Other people identify themselves as being *intellectual* and spend most of their time in intellectual thinking, and behaving according to the *higher feelings and actions* of vijnanamaya kosha.

We can't talk about the experience of the few who 'live' at the level of anandamaya kosha; we should just keep quiet and listen to their wisdom.

Where to now?

We have looked at our wonderful human heritage that is inherent in the koshas. We have seen how an understanding of the koshas can give us an overall perspective of the human individual and the vast potential of each of us. Let us now look at how we can develop that potential by examining a fundamental foundation of human personality and development – the chakra system.

3

The Chakra Systems – Centres of Unity

How we perceive our world, how we think, our emotions and our behaviour are all unique to each one of us, and they help determine how we interact in the world in one way or another. Our memories are important factors here in governing what we will do in each of these aspects of our experience.

However, we have another important dimension of characteristics which are related to the different aspects of our personalities. They determine:

· What aspects of our *sensations* and perceptions will be most *meaningful* for us.
· What our most *significant memories* are.
· What especially drives our *thinking patterns*.
· What our *'favourite' emotions* are.
· What our most *likely behaviour* patterns are.

These characteristics are connected to a system of centres in the individual called chakras. The chakras are little known to Western science, but they have been a fundamental linchpin on which the science of yoga has been based for thousands of years. We will deal with the chakras in this chapter, and integrate them with what we have already discussed.

The chakras – what are they?
The word *chakra* means 'wheel' in the Sanskrit language. They are called this because they are seen clairvoyantly as

a series of wheel-like vortexes of energy in a person. As discussed in the previous chapter in relation to pranamaya kosha, yoga describes a subtle network of energy within the physical body which flows in channels called nadis. At the main points where nadis intersect there is a chakra, which is considered in the energy body to be a kind of energy modulator or transducer, and in the 'mind' bodies as a switch for the different aspects of the personality. There are seven major chakras, which are situated along the spinal axis.

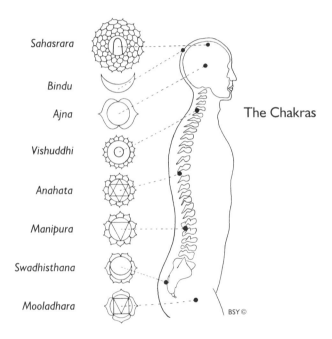

Sahasrara

Bindu

Ajna

The Chakras

Vishuddhi

Anahata

Manipura

Swadhisthana

Mooladhara

BSY ©

Those main chakras are, starting from the lower end:
- *Mooladhara chakra* at the floor of the perineum.
- *Swadhisthana chakra* at the sacrum.
- *Manipura chakra* in the spinal area behind the navel.
- *Anahata chakra* in the spinal area behind the heart.
- *Vishuddhi chakra* in the spinal area behind the throat.
- *Ajna chakra* (pronounced 'aagnya)' in the centre of the brain behind the point between the eyebrows.

- *Sahasrara* at the top of the head. It is not actually a chakra but the culmination of the evolution of all the other six chakras. We work on the other six.

The main chakras represent different aspects of the personality, the psychic qualities, and also the physical and vital aspects.

In this book not many Sanskrit names are introduced in order to make it easier for the beginner, but it is necessary to learn the names of the chakras. Why?

- There are only seven of them, so why not?
- Because they will be referred to constantly from now on.
- The name of each chakra, if pronounced properly, is actually a mantra that activates that chakra.

So the chakras are discrete centres. They are represented in the structure of the individual's body, energy system and mental system, and they influence our psychic and spiritual awareness. We will be dealing with the six main ones from their psychological perspective, although we should remember that the chakras link all the dimensions (koshas) of the person.

Remember that:

1. The physical components of the chakras such as the nerve plexuses, endocrine glands and surrounding muscles/joints are involved in the other chakra activities, and form an important link in the *body/energy/mind complex.* They are also an important link in the formation of psychosomatic illness, and are a main route by which the physical practices of yoga affect the mind and vitality. We will deal with them later.

2. Some ways in which the chakras influence the mind may be through direct physical connection along the paths of the nervous system, then into the appropriate personality areas of the brain.

3. There is a whole section of yogic teaching – *pranayama* – that deals with the energy system – purification, expansion and balancing of the whole vitality. It is considered crucially important for the physical, mental, psychic and spiritual

wellbeing of the person. The energy components of the chakras constitute an important part of this, which we will discuss later.

4. An important point when viewing human troubles and potentials from the chakra aspect is that one of the main functions of Satyananda Yoga practices is to act directly on our chakras, and evolve our different personality qualities in that way.

As we have discussed, yoga tells us, and so does Western psychology, that we respond to our world because of the deep memories of our past experiences. The practices of yoga allow us to know those memories and to learn from them.

With yoga we also discover that we have a number of principal aspects to our personalities: our sense of security, joy, sexuality, power, dynamic action, self-esteem, love, ability to communicate, intellect and intuition, and that these are associated with the main chakras. We work with the chakras to evolve those aspects of our nature. We will be exploring these memories and chakras to learn how this is done.

Personality aspects of the chakras

- *Mooladhara* chakra deals in general with one's personal security, with getting and keeping money and material possessions, and some say with the aspect of sexuality or reproducing progeny.
- *Swadhisthana* chakra deals with joy, humour, the enjoyment of sexuality, and seeking pleasure in general.
- *Manipura* chakra deals with personal power, dynamic action to get things done, and self-esteem.
- *Anahata* chakra, the heart chakra, deals with love, compassion, emotions and other feelings.
- *Vishuddhi* chakra, among a number of things, deals with communication and interpersonal relationships.
- *Ajna* chakra deals with intellect, intuition, wisdom, certain higher powers and psychic abilities.

39

• *Sahasrara* is the centre of enlightenment, the highest attainments of all the other centres.

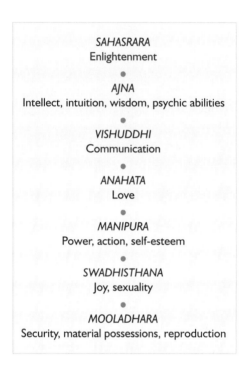

SAHASRARA
Enlightenment
●
AJNA
Intellect, intuition, wisdom, psychic abilities
●
VISHUDDHI
Communication
●
ANAHATA
Love
●
MANIPURA
Power, action, self-esteem
●
SWADHISTHANA
Joy, sexuality
●
MOOLADHARA
Security, material possessions, reproduction

Relationship of the chakras to each other

It is common to look upon the chakras as having an 'order of merit' from the bottom to the top – the lower ones of possessiveness, sexuality and power at the bottom of the 'merit scale', and the higher ones of love, communication and intellect/intuition at the top. There is value in this viewpoint for a number of reasons.

1. Although all the chakras are associated with the physical body, especially the endocrine glands, and also relate to all the different koshas, mooladhara and swadhisthana chakras at the lower end deal with survival and sexuality, which are common to all animals. In contrast, ajna chakra at the upper end is related to intellect, intuition

40

and the psychic realms – very human qualities. So in some respects the chakras represent progressively higher states of awareness, the higher chakras being more and more subtle in their expression. In this respect, the ascent of consciousness through the chakras is a representation of the spiritual path.

2. It is easier for the higher qualities of the upper chakras to evolve if the 'traps', especially greed, lust and power hunger, concealed in the lower chakras have been worked through. We know of many people who seem to reach great spiritual heights by concentrating on developing the positive aspects of the upper chakras. Then they fall (from that great height) because of one (or more) of the lower three instincts that have been 'lying in wait' for them. This is one very good reason why Satyananda Yoga teaches us to work on all the chakras at the one time. The only time it is good to specialize in a chakra is when the spiritual master has told us in person (not in dream or fantasy) to do so.

In *Kundalini Tantra* Swami Satyananda wrote:

All life is evolving and mankind is no exception. Human evolution, the evolution which we are undergoing relentlessly, both as individuals and as a race, is a journey through the different chakras. Mooladhara is the most basic, fundamental chakra from where we commence our evolution, and sahasrara is where our evolution is completed.

However, if we also look at all the chakra systems, it is obvious that the personality qualities of *each chakra* have higher and lower degrees of evolvement in each of us. Certainly each of us has personality aspects of each chakra evolved to different degrees in different orders. As well as that, we can evolve individual chakra aspects. We will be looking at them from this point of view, in which all the chakras and their manifestations are considered in the same light. In this case the 'higher and lower' qualities are within each chakra complex, represented by the degree of evolution of the aspects of that chakra. We can imagine our evolution of the individual qualities as a vertical scale through each chakra as in the diagram below.

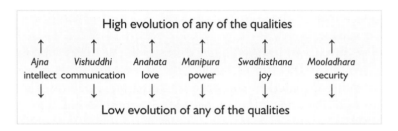

Personality differences

Looking at the personality from the viewpoint of the chakras, we can see that, not only does each chakra represent a different group of personality characteristics, but there are two other areas in which we differ from each other.

1. There are differing degrees of *evolution* of each aspect of the chakras. We will discuss the model of this evolution in the next chapter, in terms of what the yogis call the gunas, and the actual evolvement in the next section (A Yogic View of Personality and its Evolvement).

2. There is differing *activity* of each of the chakra systems in each individual, which lead to differing strengths of expression of the aspects of each chakra. We will discuss this in detail later as well.

4

The Gunas –
Steps of Evolvement

Yoga is about evolvement of the individual, so we might expect that there are various models of evolvement within yoga itself, and this is true. For instance, the whole idea of the koshas is of different levels of evolvement from the physical level to the energy level, to the lower mind, through the higher mind, right up through what may be called the 'super-mind'. The chakras themselves are another model of evolution because, as mentioned, the preservation of the body that is reflected in *mooladhara* chakra is a very basic instinct of all living things, as are the drives to reproduce the species of *swadhisthana*, and the will to power of *manipura*. Higher than this are the love and nurturing of *anahata* chakra, the very human communication styles of *vishuddhi*, and the ability of high level thinking and intuition which are inherent in *ajna* chakra.

However, yoga has a quite specific way of describing the degree of evolution in the individual and indeed within all matter – this is the gunas.

What are the gunas?

In their widest sense these are qualities of all creative nature, described by Sri Krishna in the *Bhagavad Gita* as purity, passion and inertia – the purity quality being known as *sattwa*, the passion quality as *rajas*, and the inertia as *tamas*. In the 14th chapter he says:

43

Purity, passion and inertia – these qualities, born of nature, bind fast in the body, the embodied, the indestructible. (v. 5)

Of these, Sattwa, which from its stainlessness is luminous and healthy, binds by attachment to happiness and by attachment to knowledge. (v. 6)

Know Rajas to be of the nature of passion, the source of thirst (for sensual enjoyment) and attachment. It binds one by attachment to action. (v. 7)

But know that Tamas is born of ignorance, deluding all embodied beings. It binds fast by heedlessness, indolence and sleep. (v. 8)

This may sound a little obscure at this point, but it becomes clearer as Sri Krishna goes on to explain at length the manifestation of these three qualities as they express themselves in a person.

It should be realized that these qualities apply to all aspects of nature, but in this book, as certainly in the Gita itself, it is applied especially to the human mind and tendencies at all levels, and clearly describes the different levels of evolution of the various thinking and behaviour states of human beings. For instance, sattwa, when it is our predominant quality at the time, influences us towards purity, happiness and knowledge; rajas, when it is the more active, influences us towards the passionate pursuit of satisfying our desires for sensual enjoyment; whereas tamas, which derives from ignorance, influences us towards heedlessness – for example, of the needs of others – laziness and sleep.

In Chapter 18 Sri Krishna again takes up the subject of the effect of our prevailing guna on our *viewpoint* of life, our *actions* and our *personal style*.

"The person mainly under the influence of *sattwa* sees the one indestructible Reality in all beings," so there is a sense of 'us' rather than 'me and them'; they perform "action which is ordained, which is free from attachment, and which is done without love or hatred by one who is not desirous of any reward," i.e. unselfish, unemotional actions for the good of all, and the person is "free from attachment, is non-egoistic, endowed with firmness and enthusiasm, and is unaffected by success or failure."

The person mainly under the influence of *rajas* "sees in all beings various entities of distinct kinds as different from one another," so their viewpoint is one of assessing others as a means of satisfying their desires; "action is done . . . longing for the fulfilment of desires or gain, with egoism or with much effort," so actions are based on "what's in it for me?" Sri Krishna describes the rajasic person most unflatteringly as "passionate, desiring to obtain the reward of actions, greedy, cruel, impure, and moved by joy and sorrow."

The person mainly influenced by *tamas* "clings to one single effect as if it were the whole, without reason, without foundation in truth." So they are fanatical and stick stubbornly to their opinions, which are not based on reason or even common sense but often will be projections of their own faults onto other people. Their "actions are undertaken from delusion, without regard for the consequences, loss, injury and (their own) ability," so their actions can be harmful to other people as well as to themselves. Sri Krishna describes people under the influence of tamas in terms they would certainly not include in their curriculum vitae, as "unsteady, vulgar, stubborn, cheating, malicious, lazy, despondent and procrastinating."

The principle is that these qualities variously influence each one of us from time to time. Sometimes one will be under the influence of sattwa, and at that time our perceptions of the world and the individuals around us, our thinking, our emotions and our tendencies to behave in certain ways will have the sattwic qualities about them. At other times these will be influenced by the rajasic qualities, and at others by the tamasic. We are a mixture of these three qualities, and we are literally pushed from this side to that, as the tides of the three gunas dominate our lives, but most of us spend most of our lives mainly under the sway of one of these gunas.

However, at times, though we are customarily under rajas or even sattwa, we can crash down into tamas and get stuck there for a time because of adverse circumstances in our lives – but more of that later.

From the point of view of the yogis, the preferable influence is that of sattwa. It is the most evolved level, closest to the highest levels of our being, and productive of our greatest progress and happiness. So the main thrust of yoga is to clear the blockages that are keeping us down in the lower levels and spend more and more time living under the influence of sattwa.

When we consider Sri Krishna's descriptions of people under the predominant influence of rajas and tamas, we are struck by the negative descriptions he gives them. One may consider that he has done this to make them stand out in stark relief compared with the sattwic properties. However, if we look at the gunas from a wider perspective, we can see all three have positive qualities if used in the right way. For instance, with rajas, planning, dynamism and activity can be sublimated for higher purposes, as can the expectation of outcomes which forms such an integral part of rajas. Even qualities of tamas can be directed in appropriate directions. The inertia and sleepiness can be well earned rest, the stuck-ness can be stability or firmness when required, the apathy can be equanimity and the stubbornness can become fortitude.

So the gunas 'colour' everything they influence with qualities, some of which are:

Sattwa

The state of truth, simplicity and equanimity in action.
· Purity
· Balance, light, clear perception, simplicity
· The essence of learning and awakening

46

- Seeking and getting knowledge
- Vision is looking for opportunities to help
- Thinking is accurate, intuitive, wise
- Emotions are positive, based on faith
- Aspiration is altruistic and ethical
- Activities are performed for the good of all
- Leads to ENLIGHTENMENT, our true state.

Rajas
The state of dynamism and activity, combined with full ego involvement.

- Passion
- The basis of all movement and planning in the world, body and mind
- It is momentum, change, movement, power, force and restlessness
- Personal vision is opportunistic
- Thinking is rational and adequate
- Emotions are positive if everything is going well
- Personal ambition, ego, effort, drive
- Activities are performed to fulfil desires and ambitions.

Tamas
The state of inertia and ignorance.

- Inertia
- Stability, lethargy, laziness
- Fatigue, dullness, apathy, feeling stuck
- Impurity, disease, ignorance, darkness
- Vision is limited to a primitive level of survival
- Thinking is illogical, bigoted, fanatical
- Emotions negative, based on survival
- Actions defensive, may be harmful
- Probability of change to improve is blocked because tamas is 'stuck-ness'
- BUT don't condemn people who are stuck down in tamas; you don't know what life experiences they have had. See their potentials.

Tools for self-knowledge

Later we will see how these gunas influence the different personality aspects as related to the different chakras, and how the combination of these forms two of the dimensions of our practical model of personality and its evolvement. First, however, we need to look at the yogic science of swara yoga. It explains the fundamental principle of balance, of the mind, emotions, behaviour – in fact of all aspects of our lives. The strange thing is that it seems to have been kept secret for thousands of years, because hardly anybody outside yoga circles knows anything about it, although it is extremely important in human life.

5

Swara Yoga –
The Balance of Life

For thousands of years yogis have known that when the right nostril is flowing more freely, in the state they call *pingala*, we are more extroverted, active, physical, warmer – the 'sun' qualities. Whereas when the left nostril is flowing more freely, in the state they call *ida*, we are more introverted, passive, 'mental', cooler – the 'moon' qualities. And when the flows are balanced, in the state they call *sushumna*, those qualities are balanced too.

This was just accepted by yogis, though not by very many other people, and most of the world had not even heard about it. However, all that has changed. There is now a solid body of scientific evidence that not only supports the above assertions, but attributes it all to the activity of one side of the brain or the other. Medical research started it all and other kinds of research have gone on from there. It is an interesting story of ancient wisdom and modern super technology in a collaboration to explain one of the fundamentals of life. Let us start with just a few facts about how the human body works.

THE CEREBRAL HEMISPHERES

In the great majority of people, about 97% of the population, the *left* side of the brain handles the production of language, and the *right* side handles spatial orientation

49

and recognition of faces and objects. How do we know this percentage? We know that about 90% of people are strongly or predominantly right-handed, and the other 10% are left-handed or ambidextrous. Almost all of the right-handers (about 99%), and about 70% of left-handers, have language controlled by the left side of the brain, while the remaining 30% of left-handers have it controlled by the right hemisphere or both. I hope the 3% whose hemispheres process information the other way will forgive me for referring in this chapter to the 'lefts' and 'rights' of the majority of people. It doesn't matter that much anyway because in yoga we don't select a hemisphere for special attention, we try to balance them both.

The *left* hemisphere is larger, with many short fibres making multiple connections, suggesting that it handles *details* in a more concentrated way. The *right* hemisphere, on the other hand, has long fibres making fewer connections at greater distances, suggesting that it deals with *wider* fields of perception and concepts. This is exactly what is found in tests on the two sides.

The bridge between the sides of the brain

The corpus callosum is a large bundle of fibres that link up the two hemispheres, so apparently the two sides of the brain are in constant communication, and instantly share with each other information about what's going on there. If this is the case, how can we detect different functions on each side? Not all information is shared.

Most functions are the same on both sides, but some are exclusive

Functions of the cerebral cortex such as motor, sensory and visual are on both sides of the brain, but some other functions specialize on one side or the other, and it is these that interest us here. The first one that was discovered was *speech* by Dr Paul Broca in 1861. He found that one section of the left frontal lobe controlled the production of speech, and

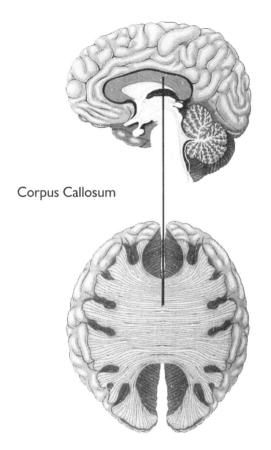

Corpus Callosum

that a person who had a stroke that affected that area lost the power of speech, whereas a stroke at the same place in the right side did not affect speech. From then on, a lot of brain mapping was done in various ways, and it looked as if we would be able to discover the discrete areas where each thing happened in the brain. But we now realize that it is not so easy, that many of the functions are complex interconnections between different areas, some a long way apart.

However, we are realizing more and more that many functions do specialize on one side only, and we have started to form a picture of the differing styles of the two sides of the brain.

The hemispheres act together

Even in the case of functions that are represented on different sides, the hemispheres act together to enrich our experience. For instance, if we are reading a story, the two hemispheres are doing different jobs. The *left* side handles the words, syntax and meanings of what we are reading – it converts the words on the paper into ideas. At the same time the *right* hemisphere is visualizing what is happening – for instance, if the story says, "The man strode confidently down the street", the *left* side reads the words and forms them into a story, while the *right* side creates a picture of the man striding down the street. The *right* side also perceives the holistic story structure – it 'strings' the whole story together, as well as assessing the emotional content of the story, the humour and the metaphor etc. The *left* side handles the details; the *right* side creates the picture and the feelings.

The split-brain experiments

Experiments on the responses of the two sides of the brain have been going on for about forty years, so the principles are well established and the research is proved to be valid. Roger Sperry did the pioneering research in this area in humans in the 1970s and won a Nobel Prize for it in 1981. He tested people who, in order to help their severe epilepsy, had previously had their corpus callosum severed, which separated the communication between the sides of the brain – the so-called 'split-brain'. Visual fields were used in the experiments because even after cutting the corpus callosum, the *right* visual field still feeds into the *left* side of the brain, and the *left* visual field into the *right* side. However, after the operation one side did not know what was going on in the visual field belonging to the other side, or what the other side of the brain thought about it. Some of his work involved recognizing words, and he was on to a winner there because we already knew that words were the domain of the *left* side. But soon he and his team were experimenting with such things as people's cognitive abilities, attitudes, moral ideas, etc., and they found that they were also specific to their own side of the brain. A lot of research has gone on since then and has opened up a very interesting field of knowledge about our human functioning.

Effects of the individual hemispheres

The question that interests us is this: How do the different sides of the brain process perception, thinking, emotion and behaviour? Do they perceive their world differently? Are their thinking patterns different? Do they experience different emotions and feelings? Do they tend to make us behave in different ways? The answers to these questions seem to be yes.

1. Perception

Speech is perceived by the *left* hemisphere, whereas the *right* hemisphere's speech ability is limited to simple names. However, the *right* hemisphere is good at perceiving spatial patterns and a sense of direction and distance in its surroundings (Joseph, 1988).[1]

Detail in the surroundings is best perceived by the *left* hemisphere, whereas the *right* hemisphere takes in the whole scene, estimating depth, position, getting the 'big picture' (Gazzaniga, 1996).[2]

The optimistic view of what is perceived is the domain of the *left* hemisphere, whereas the *right* hemisphere perceives the environment in a much more cautious and pessimistic way. Experiments using the visual fields showed that responses to ambiguous situations elicited a more guarded response from the *right* side. In one experiment, cards with misty indefinite pictures were presented to split-brain subjects. Identical pictures of each scene were presented to each visual field, but because they were out of order the subjects couldn't remember what response they had given to the picture when they had seen it on the other side, or even if they had seen it. When a picture was shown to the *right* visual field (*left* hemisphere) the subjects gave a much more positive assessment of what was going on in the picture than

53

when it was shown to the left visual field (*right* hemisphere) – in each case the same person would give very different responses to the same picture.

A lot of observation has been made over many years of people who had damage to various parts of their brains from injury, stroke, tumour, surgery, etc. When applied more recently to this study of hemisphere dominance, it has shown that each side seems to balance the other side's responses to outside events. People who have lesions on the left side often respond to mild negative situations with 'catastrophic emotions' – obviously the right side out of control. People with lesions on the right side respond to the same stimuli, no matter how serious, with casual nonchalance ('la belle indifférence') – obviously the left side taking its optimism too far.

Positive and negative situations. Not only do we make a positive or negative assessment of something in our surroundings, depending on whether it is perceived by the left or the right hemisphere, but it has also been shown that it goes the other way; positive situations (e.g. friendly) activate the *left* hemisphere, and negative situations (e.g. threatening) activate the *right.*

Schiffer *et al.* (1998) showed, by asking split-brain people questions of a psychological nature, that the right hemisphere was more disturbed by negative childhood memories than the left.[3]

A number of tests have been done showing pictures of sad and happy faces to these people (e.g. Duda *et al.*, 1984, McLaren *et al.*, 1987) and they resulted in the right hemisphere responding quicker to both, even the happy faces, but we also know that recognition of facial expressions is a special skill of the right hemisphere anyway.[4, 5]

2. Thinking

Tests have shown that the *left* hemisphere handles logical, verbal, mathematical and analytical tasks, whereas the *right* is intuitive, integrative, and deals with patterns, facial identification, emotional facial expressions, etc.

EEG monitoring of people who were undergoing aptitude testing showed that *left* hemisphere activity increased during verbal tasks, and *right* activity increased during spatial tasks (Davidson, 1990, Shannahoff-Khalsa *et al.*, 1986).[6, 7]

Visual field testing showed that even in people *without* 'split-brains', verbal tasks are done better when they are presented from the right visual field, and facial identity is performed better from the left field (Levick, 1993).[8]

3. Emotion

For over 160 years since Broca found that speech is produced in the *left* frontal area, scientists have been studying *cognitive* processes all over the brain. What about the *affective* processes – the emotions? The researchers have done much less until recently, but now this important area is being investigated using modern brain imaging techniques. For instance, Richard Davidson at the University of Wisconsin did research using a new technique called Functional Magnetic Resonance Imaging (MRI) which produces three-dimensional images of the brain, with different colours showing the different levels of activity in each part. In almost 200 people, he found that when they have high brain activity in the *left middle frontal gyrus,* a specific site in the front of the *left* side of the brain, they report '*positive*' feelings such as happiness, enthusiasm, joy, high energy and alertness. In contrast, those people who had more activity in the *right* middle frontal gyrus reported such *negative* emotions as pessimism, dejection, low energy and even depression. These results have been supported in further research.

Other experiments have also shown that if we purposely change our emotions, for example, from sadness to happiness or the reverse, the activities in the hemispheres change sides.

4. Behaviour

We know that language is produced by the left hemisphere, but not much research has been done on how the activities of the sides of the brain affect our other behaviour, though we could assume that the way we tend to behave will follow on from our perceptions, thinking and emotions as it usually does. This would certainly agree with the outgoing, extroverted, positive, adventurous tendencies being associated with the left side of the brain, and the in-turning, introverted, guarded, conservative tendencies with the right side. It is interesting that some of the personality tests identify two principal personality factors: *introversion–extroversion* and *neuroticism–non-neuroticism*; just what we have been discussing in terms of swara yoga and evolvement of the individual. The three other accepted personality factors, *openness, agreeableness* and *conscientiousness,* can be seen to equate also with either the hemisphere activity or evolvement.

The positive qualities of the right brain

The above apparently 'negative' qualities associated with the right brain are, of course, the manifestations of that part of the brain as it subserves the ordinary instincts of self-preservation, reproduction and nurturing – the rajasic and tamasic levels. At the higher level of evolution the *right* side is the area of music awareness, art awareness, three-dimensional perception, creativity, imagination, insight, intuition and higher powers. The balancing of 'ida and pingala' at that level then becomes the blending of these qualities of the *right* side with the *left* side qualities of language (written and spoken), number skills, rational decision-making, accurate judgement and discrimination. This is an excellent degree of ability if we can maintain that level and harmony.

The implications of these findings for our personality balance are very important for our day-to-day life, and yogis have realized this for a long time. They didn't know about the involvement of the hemispheres of the brain, of course, but they did notice the fluctuations of mood and behaviour associated with the flow of air through the respective nostrils, and that forms the second part of the recent research.

56

THE NOSTRILS

First a few observations about the structure of the nostrils.

Mucous membrane

This is the soft moist skin that covers the insides of the whole respiratory tract. It secretes mucus which moistens the incoming air, and traps dust particles, germs and other foreign bodies before they can go down into the lungs. The cells of the mucous membrane have small projections called cilia, which cover the whole surface in the form of the hair-like pile of a carpet. They constantly wave backwards and forwards in rhythm, almost like a large conveyor belt, and move the mucus, with its load of dust, bacteria, viruses, etc., up out of the lungs and nostrils to the pharynx, from which it can be spat out or go down into the stomach.

Most people don't realize this, but within the mucous membrane of the nostrils there is what is called erectile tissue (similar to that in the genitals), which can fill up with blood, and swell the mucous membranes so that the nostril space is partially blocked. In this way the nostrils can be alternately blocked and dilated from side to side, as we shall see.

Turbinates

These are three projections on the lateral walls of each nostril. They create turbulence in the air flowing in and out of the nostrils, so that the air comes into contact with the mucous membranes as much as possible, to moisten it, clear it and warm it. They also fill space in the nostrils, so that as the mucous membrane swells, most of the nostril is blocked, and the airflow is impeded. The nostril can also be blocked by inflamed bulbous swellings of the mucous membranes called polyps, which can be easily removed by an appropriate surgeon, and can sometimes be shrunk by a yoga practice called neti.

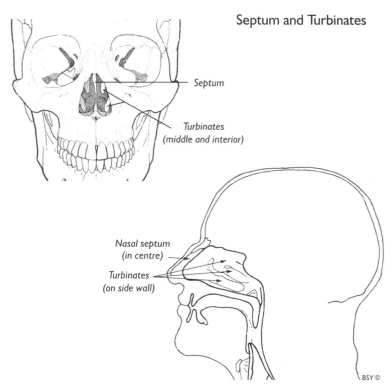

Septum and Turbinates

Septum

Turbinates
(middle and interior)

Nasal septum
(in centre)

Turbinates
(on side wall)

BSY ©

Septum

This is the vertical wall of tissue in the centre of the nose that divides the nostrils from each other. In the front it is made of cartilage, but towards the back of the nose it is a thin sheet of bone. Some people have this deviated over to one side, usually as a result of injury. It is known as 'deviation of the septum', and it can completely and continuously block the nostril on one side, causing problems as we shall see.

Air preparation

The nostrils prepare the air for the lungs; they warm and moisten it and eliminate the dust. On the way out, the opposite occurs; the air warmed by the lungs warms the nose.

Hemispheres and nostrils

David Shannahoff-Khalsa (1993) at the University of San Diego used EEG testing to assess which side of the brain was most active as the nostril flow was monitored. He found that, as the yogis would have expected, it was the opposite side to the one with the more open nostril. If the right nostril was flowing more, the left side of the brain was more active; if the left nostril was flowing more, the right hemisphere was more active. He also found that when the nostril flow changed to the other side, the opposite hemisphere became activated.[9] He supported the claims the swara yogis had been making for thousands of years that nostril flow provokes within us the type of perception, thinking, emotions and behaviour we now associate with the two hemispheres of the brain, although the ancient yogis of course described this in more symbolical language.

Daily rhythms of nostril dilation and constriction

Yoga tells us that in each one of us there is a daily rhythm of nostril dilation and constriction from side to side, which they call the *swara*. At some point, one nostril is *constricted* by the engorgement of its mucous membrane's erectile tissue, and the nostril on the other side is *open* due to narrowing of the blood vessels in its mucous membrane. Then gradually the situation reverses, and this to-ing and fro-ing continues. This cycle varies in people, but is generally repeated every 1½ to 3 hours for the whole 24 hours of the day, every day. Shannahoff-Khalsa also confirmed this, as so many of us have done, by simply checking at regular times (each half hour is a good time) which nostril is flowing more freely, and noting it down.

According to the yogic teachings, when the breath is flowing freest in the *right* nostril (*left* brain), it is the best time to do active, outgoing, assertive and teaching activities. When the breath is flowing more in the *left* nostril (*right* brain), it is a better time for passive, quiet, submissive and learning interactions. In the periods between the alternate flows,

59

when both nostrils are flowing evenly, it is the best time to not be interacting at all, but to be meditating.

Aptitude tests

Shannahoff-Khalsa (1991) and his team also tested how well people did on verbal tasks or spatial tasks. He gave standardized tests of verbal ability and spatial ability to people, noted their results and also noted which of their nostrils was flowing at the time. He found that aptitude coincided with the openess of the right or left nostril – all the people generally did better on *verbal* tasks when their right nostril was flowing (*left* hemisphere) and better on *spatial* tests when their left nostril was flowing (*right* hemisphere).[10]

IMPLICATIONS OF SWARA YOGA

A side for all occasions

If we look at the tendencies of the two sides, we will see something interesting: each side subserves one aspect of the self-preservation/reproduction instincts that are inherent in the body/mind.

Perception: The *right* brain mechanism perceives the world in big holistic pictures – just the thing for spotting any irregularities such as movements or shapes in our surroundings that might mean a hungry predator, a meal or a mate. This sounds the alert, the instantaneous cautionary stance. Then the *left* brain comes in and analyses the stimulus. It may not be a thing to be avoided, maybe it's a feed or a potential mate, so I can approach it and benefit from it.

Thinking: Based on the information from perception, the mind will assess the danger (to be avoided) or attractiveness (a meal or a mate – to be approached) and the best course of action. According to which it is, the thinking style of the appropriate side – right hemisphere for avoidance, left hemisphere for approach – will be activated.

Emotion: If the object is dangerous, the right side of the brain will go into action and one of the typical fear/withdrawal emotions will occur and motivate the animal to avoid the situation. If it is attractive, the left brain will provoke one of the outgoing emotions such as joy/pleasant anticipation or hungry/hunter, which will induce it to approach the object.

Behaviour: The appropriate behavioural responses from one or other of the hemispheres will be automatic and instantaneous in all except the majority of humans and trained animals.

Unbalanced?

Our ideal state is to have the flow through the nostrils mainly balanced, so that it is easy to move into either of the responses, depending on which is appropriate. The main problem comes when a person is stuck in one modality continuously, such as when one nostril is permanently blocked. Then, depending on which side is blocked, one's whole life can take on the 'colouring' of that side.

1. If the *right* nostril is continuously *blocked* (left nostril open), so the *right* side of the brain dominates, the person will see their world in an overcautious or pessimistic way, think in a self-preservative way, tend to feel the emotions of fear, anxiety, pessimism, dejection and maybe depression, and behave in an avoidant way.

2. If the *left* nostril is continuously blocked (right nostril open) so the *left* side of the brain dominates, the person will tend to be undercautious, daring, maybe careless, may fail to see the 'warning signs' in their world and relationships. They will think in a positive but often inappropriate way, feel the emotions of positive anticipation, maybe even elation, and may 'step in where angels fear to tread'.

This makes one wonder if there is an element of this in some of the depressive and manic behaviour patterns some people experience.

The big swings

Another problem is that some people have extreme swings in their swara rhythm during the day; each nostril spending hours fully blocked, only to be replaced by the complete blockage of the other for more hours. These people tend to have emotional instability during the whole day, spending hours dejected, depressed or anxious, then irritable, angry or elated for a few hours. In both instances the emotions and behaviour are not appropriate to the circumstances at the time.

Needless to say this is very frustrating for the person, and for the other people in their lives. They need to balance the flow through their nostrils, and yoga has many practices to do this. The neti group of nasal practices is a specific example, but actually a balanced group of yoga relaxation, postures, breath practices and meditation will balance the swara over time if the nostrils are otherwise physically normal.

What should we do?

We should try to keep the flow of the air through our nostrils reasonably balanced. There is no need to become obsessed with this; most people have a slightly uneven flow and it doesn't seem to affect them. However, if it is extreme, and especially if one is obviously being affected by this, one may need to rectify the problem with yoga, and may even need to have a polyp removed, or a badly deviated nasal septum straightened surgically.

We can also change the flow of the nostrils temporarily by some simple practices. For example:

1. Try this now. Check which nostril is flowing more easily by blocking the front of each nostril in turn and assessing the breath through the other. Then on the side with the better flow put your fist or a fairly thick book or a pillow in the armpit, and gently press down on it. Within a short time – sometimes only seconds – the previously blocked nostril on the other side will open and flow more easily.
2. Simply lie down on the side on which the nostril is flowing better, and soon the nostril on the high side will open.
3. For a period of time breathe only through the partially blocked nostril, and after a while it will open.

Taking a balanced view

We have discussed the koshas and the vast range of consciousness that makes up the human being. We have looked at the chakras, the centres that subserve the different aspects of our personality. We have realized the range of evolution of these aspects as explained by the gunas. We have seen the intimate relationship between the flow of air through our nostrils and the balance of our personality, as explained by swara yoga. Now to round off this short overview of yoga, we need to look at another dimension of our personality model – understanding the human mind. We will see what the yogis tell us about it, how this compares with the viewpoints of Western psychology, and how it fits into this 'big picture' of the human individual we are painting.

6

The Mind and Personality

The yogic view of human personality and how to develop it has some answers that are very similar to conclusions reached independently by Western psychologists. However, some of them are very different and they should be given much more attention in the West.

This chapter deals with how we respond to the world around us, and is so similar to the Western point of view that they really correspond with each other. We have looked at the concepts of chakras and gunas, which have been fundamental to yogic understanding for thousands of years, but have been unheard of in the West. How these two perspectives come together to give us a *valid and practical model of personality* is interesting and instructive, and also gives us a way of evolving our personalities through the techniques and lifestyle practices of yoga.

As well as self-improvement, the principles and practices of yoga have been proved to be so effective in dealing with neurotic and personality problems that in the opinion of this psychiatrist, Western psychology, psychotherapy and psychiatry will do their clients a great service by using yoga in their therapies.

As we are dealing here with human personality, we need to agree on what it is. As you might imagine, there are many definitions of personality. The word itself starts with an interesting concept – the 'persona'. This was a mask worn by certain actors in ancient times to represent different characters, and implies that 'personality' is the external appearance which hides the internal reality. The psychiatrist C.G. Jung of early last century took up this idea, and used the word for just that, the person's social façade or front that enabled their deeper reality to function in this world. Modern psychologists have widened that idea to include the unique characteristics that they conceive of as making me 'me', and you 'you'.

WHAT IS PERSONALITY?

The distinctive and characteristic patterns of *perception, memory, thought, emotions and behaviour* that define an individual's *personal style* of interacting with the physical and social environments.

This definition is based on the one in Hilgard's *Introduction to Psychology*[1], which only includes 'thought, emotion and behaviour'. It emphasizes that:

1. Each personality is unique to ('characteristic' of) that person, and is 'distinctive' in that it distinguishes his or her *patterns of expression* from those of other people. We have many similarities with each other too, especially if we grow up in the same culture, and these also contribute to our personal style of interacting with our world. But the people who study personality are keen to concentrate on individual differences that make us unique. Just continue to remember our similarities though, because they also can hold us back from evolving to our highest potential.

2. These *patterns* are the different ways in which we *perceive* our world, how our unique set of *memories* influences that perception and what we *think* of it, the typical *emotions* that result, and our customary ways of then *behaving* or not behaving. We will take these one by one, see how they are unique to each one of us, and later discuss how other aspects of our being, such as the chakras and the gunas, influence them.

3. According to how each one of us responds in this way, we will interact in our own unique way with the individuals around us, and with the world we live in.

The mind and how it affects our interactions with our world

Remember that the higher animals all have the same sort of instinctual responses we are about to describe. However, in addition to that we, as humans, have the ability for higher thinking and behaviour. The main way we interact with our world and the people around us at the *instinctual* level though is explained below.

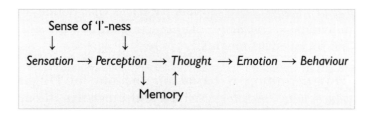

Some things to note:

1. *Yoga agrees*: This is an area where the yogis and western psychologists agree, and we have Sanskrit names for these as mentioned in Chapter 2 on the koshas:
   a) The sense of 'I'-ness is called *ahamkara*.
   b) The organs of sensation are called the *jnanendriyas*.
   c) Memory is called *chitta*.
   d) The mind functions – perception, thought and emotion – are *manas*.
   e) The intellectual mind is *buddhi*.

2. *'I'-ness*: The sense of *'I'-ness*, or of being individuals (*ahamkara*), which separates 'me' from 'you' or 'it', is necessary for self-preservation and the process of clear perception. Some people with schizophrenia or brain damage, or those under the influence of psychedelic drugs, have a weak sense of 'I'-ness, a blurred sense of self, so their perception is faulty. This then affects their thinking, emotions and

behaviour. Other people who have a strong sense of 'I'-ness, of separateness, can be isolated from people.

3. *Perception*: What is perception? It is the process whereby a person's sensory stimuli are translated into *organized experiences that have personal meaning for him or her.* For example, when we see something 'out there', the retina of our eyes receives the millions of spots of coloured light that come in. These are then converted into nerve impulses which travel to the visual cortex of the brain, and by the process of *perception* they are translated into whole experiences that have personal meaning for us, such as the form of a person we recognize.

4. *Memory*: When 'I' perceive something, it is instantly checked with my memory stores. "Have I seen one of these before?" "What is it?" "What *meaning* has it had for me in the past?" Then the mind takes over. But from the viewpoint of yoga there is more to this activity than is generally thought.

5. *Mind*: Basically the mind thinks, "That's a lion coming, I want to avoid it" or "That's my loved one, I want to embrace her/him." There may be other variations on this theme, but the main concern of the instinctual mind is self-preservation and preservation of the species. This fundamentally means attraction to pleasurable experiences such as food and sex, and avoidance of painful experiences such as an encounter with the lion.

6. *Emotion*: If real action is called for, it is usually 'energized' by an emotion, which gives urgency to and motivates the whole operation.

7. *Action*: At this instinctual level – the level of the un-trained animal – if the perception is meaningful enough to cause an emotion, it will automatically go on to some sort of behaviour. This is usually an action such as attacking if the animal is angry or hungry, escaping or playing dead if it is afraid, or a reflex such as wagging the tail if it is happy. Some human beings are still at this level. At the higher human level, rational intellectual thinking intervenes, and we can decide on better ways to act, or not to act. If we decide to act,

we assess what is likely to be the most appropriate thing to do, and how best to do it. But let's look at the basic responses first; we humans still use them a lot!

Let's look at these responses in more detail.

PERCEPTION

Each of us perceives the world differently. It is impossible for people to be aware of everything that is in their field of the senses such as sight, sound, touch, or even smells or taste; there is just too much. So perception chooses those objects and events that have meaning for us as an individual, concentrates on those, and ignores all the rest.

Some of the inputs of sensation and the perceptions formed from them have meaning for every one of us and catch our attention easily, such as a loved one approaching, or the lion attacking, or some traumatic event. But most are unique, and their significance depends on our own past experience. Some are even coloured by the way we feel in the present; we project our mood onto the world around us. For instance, when we are 'in love', the loved one looks beautiful, but when we are angry with them, they don't look so good after all. Fear also colours our world in dangerous hues.

Other perceptions are instinctual and largely unconscious, such as seeing a sudden movement in a still background, which quickly catches the attention. This is an important cue in any animal with eyes, and alerts it to the possibility of an enemy, a meal, or a partner.

Because our perceptions of this same world are so different, we each seem to live in a different world, so our responses are different. When we are with another person, we assume that they are experiencing the world as we are, but this is just not true. No wonder we often can't understand why other people respond as they do; they are living in a 'different' world.

As we advance in yoga, we clear out our old memories, attitudes, suppositions, preconceptions, blockages, etc., and start to see the world and other people without projecting onto them the old stuff that is really inside our own head. As our perceptions of them change, our thoughts, emotions and behaviour towards them change in a very positive way, and our relationships and contribution to society improve. This is certainly *evolvement* in action.

MEMORY

Memory is considered to be of three types: *sensory memory*, the instantaneous memory of a sensation before it goes to *short term memory* (also called working memory), which is the memories of the things we are mentally working on at this time (like the RAM in a computer), and *long term memory* (like the HDD in a computer), which is the long term storage of information. We are interested here in the latter, and especially one part of it.

Long term memory

This is also in three parts, which are given different names, but we can simply call them:

- *Personal memory* – These are the memories of our previous *experiences*, including the situations in which they happened. This is the one that is important to us here.
- *Factual memory* – The information about *facts* in our lives such as how to get home, our phone number, who the prime minister is etc.
- *Skill memory* – The instructions about how to carry out different *skills* such as driving a car, tying our shoe laces, writing etc.

The *personal memories* of each of us are, of course, very different. For example, some people's memories are full of tumultuously emotional experiences, other people have fairly emotionally neutral memories. Some people's memories of their past experiences of *security* will be calm and pleasant, for others the memories will be of fear and worry. The latter group will be more vulnerable to supposed threats to

69

their security than the contented group, and they will often perceive the same situation as being more threatening. The same applies to experiences of joy or misery, pleasure or pain, and the quality of sexual experiences. In the same way our experiences regarding power, self-esteem, love relationships, personal communications and thinking patterns will all have been different, for better or worse. Obviously they will affect our strengths and vulnerabilities when we are responding to the situations that life throws at us, and the negative ones hold us down in lower levels of our evolvement.

Some memories contain the deep instinctual drives and the desires that stem from them, as well as the strong experiences of fear, hurt, etc., which are unacceptable for us to realize. They are so emotionally painful that at some level of our consciousness we don't want to know about them at all, so they have been covered over by *repression* and other defensive mental mechanisms. These especially are the ones that cause us fear, grief, anger, shame, guilt, and affect our lives in so many ways. Even though these mental contents are deep down out of our awareness, they still have a strong effect on the way we perceive our world, our attitudes about it, our emotions and our behaviour. One of the most important ways yoga helps us is by allowing us to bring these to the surface, become aware of them, neutralize them, and strip them of their negative power over us.

Yoga says: "Learn to know yourself" and it teaches us ways to do just that, and how to get the energy of the negative impressions out of our memories. It also tells us to be careful what we put into our memories now, to limit the negative impressions and concentrate on taking in the positive impressions.

Subtle inputs

There are many influences that affect our consciousness of which we are not aware, but which still drive our thinking, attitudes, emotions and behaviour. They include the repressed *memory* traces that are already there, and our *higher levels* of consciousness. But there are also ongoing forms of input that are beyond our conscious awareness. Some examples are:

Community unconscious mind – The subtle ongoing mental and emotional inputs from our family, our friends, our neighbourhood group, our cultural group, our national psyche and the human race in general. These inputs are of two types: those attitudes that are in our *memories* due to our being influenced by these groups in the past, and the ongoing inputs that are *entering* our minds all the time. Don't ignore these, they are important, especially because we are usually totally unaware of them; we take the attitudes we derive from them as natural truth. Indeed they form our whole life paradigm. We never even question them until our attention is directed to them by a mentor, by living in another culture, or by broadening our outlook by yoga practices. How do we absorb some of these subtle inputs from other people?

1. *Body language* – These are the subliminal body expressions, movements, postures, smells, etc., that reveal to our unconscious mind how other people are really feeling. The idea, of course, is to become aware of these. A part of the training of a psychiatrist includes developing the ability to 'read' people's behaviour in this way, so that we come to know what the person is 'not saying'. Some of our most useful insights about people can come from the interpretation of these hidden communications. In most cases though, people 'pick up' this information at a subliminal level anyway, and it contributes to the decisions we make with regard to other people.

2. *Transmission of emotions from the people around us* – We continuously experience the effects of the emotional states of the people we are with, and this affects our behaviour towards them. If the other person is happy, sad, loving, angry, frightened, etc., even though they try to hide it, the emotion is transmitted to us as an 'energy' field and we experience it at some level of our consciousness. One of the

71

things that makes psychiatry and clinical psychology difficult is this absorption of negative energy all day while consulting with people.

3. *Telepathic input* – The transmission of thoughts between one person and another has been proved conclusively by the parapsychologists. Back in the 1930s Joseph B. Rhine at Duke University, USA, did the original, good quality scientific investigation, and in recent years much more sophisticated research has confirmed it. But we didn't need scientific proof – probably each one of us has experienced thinking of someone we haven't heard from for a long time, only to have that person phone us right then. Or we have felt uneasy about a loved one and when we contact them, they tell us they are in trouble. This happens too often to be just coincidence.

However, these are only examples of telepathy we are conscious of. The parapsychologists, in scientific experiments, have established that telepathy of which we are unaware can also affect us. They also suggest that at any time we are immersed in a telepathic 'conversation' with all the people in our group who are thinking of us, especially if they are doing so with emotion.

If this telepathic input is influencing our thoughts, emotions, decisions and behaviour in some subtle way, how do we stay positive? The answer is that like attracts like. If we clear out the negative stuff of our mind – and yoga does just this – our mental state becomes more positive. Then we attract the positive thoughts from out there and the negative ones just pass us by. I don't want to overstate this telepathic input, it is probably only a minor effect, but it is a good reason for us to stay positive, and to keep away from environments of low animal passions. It is also one good reason (there are others) why we should not practise powerful techniques that open up our occult powers until we have cleared out our mental 'garbage'.

4. *Precognition* – This is the ability to see into the future. So many people want to be able to do this; they don't

realize that they are probably doing it all the time. Many experiments in recent times have clearly demonstrated that some part of our consciousness is in touch with the future, and that it influences us in our decision-making, possibly all the time. This seems ridiculous to those people who have not become aware of their ability to experience events of the future. But *time* is not actually the 'horizontal line from the past into the future, with the present time here in the middle', as it seems in this wide-awake level of consciousness. As quantum physics suggests, *time* is all here at the one 'time' – we just have to switch our awareness to another level to experience other time realities.

Moreover, experiments have clearly demonstrated that we are continually aware of these 'possible futures' at some level of our consciousness. Some parapsychologists suggest that this non-conscious precognition even explains luck, that at some level we actually know what is going to happen, and that *good luck* is our unconscious mind giving us 'permission' to take positive advantage of it. *Bad luck* is our unconscious mind denying us the privilege. There are enormous implications in this for our lives, and it is thought-provoking in such attitudes as our generosity, compassion and self-esteem.

5. *Clairvoyance* – In the same way that we are receiving other psychic input, it seems from experiments that we can 'see' at levels other than just the eyes, such as 'seeing' people's auras. And it seems that this goes on continually at other levels of our consciousness, supplying information to us which contributes to our perceptions, thoughts, attitudes, feelings and responses to people and situations.

6. *Intuition* – This is 'just knowing' something, without the information coming in through our senses or from subtle levels such as we have just been discussing. According to the yogis, all knowledge is available at some level of consciousness and we only need to tune into this level for it to become available to us. One viewpoint has postulated what are called the akashic records, where all knowledge

73

is stored and can be retrieved by us from the right level of consciousness. Imagine having the right information always available to us so that we can make unerring decisions. It is said that the great yogic adepts have that ability, and they attained it through expanding their awareness with yoga.

THOUGHTS

If we look at the diagrams given on pages 79 and 80 we will see that the process of thought can be started by what we perceive in our world. If we see a snake approaching, the thought, "That's a snake, they're dangerous, I've got to get away from it" is obvious. That is, of course unless one is a snake handler by profession, in which case the thought could be completely different. I'm not joking here, because this illustrates that the way we think about our world is very dependent on our past experiences. In this way, the thinking pattern directs our behaviour; it determines whether we try to *avoid* what we see, or to *approach* it.

So the mind processes the input and tries to give it relevance, with the object of making a decision. The process goes through a number of stages, but they can happen so quickly that we don't even notice. The stages are as follows:

Identification – The mind identifies the object or what is going on. What is that thing or situation out there?

Relevance – It decides whether it is relevant for me.

Comparison – If relevant, it compares the thing or situation with similar ones in my memory.

Assessment – Then based on the information from the memory, it assesses whether it is useful or useless, harmless or harmful, important or unimportant etc.

Judgement – It then judges whether it is good or bad, right or wrong, I like it or dislike it, I agree or disagree, etc.

Decision – The mind finally decides what to do about it, generally whether to approach it, avoid it or do nothing.

As yoga develops our ability to watch our thoughts, we can often see these different stages of decision-making going on in our own mind. We can then recognize old habits of mind based on these six steps, and decide what to do about them.

The approach-avoidance information that is essential to save us from harm (avoidance) and find food or a mate (approach) goes on at virtually all levels of the animal kingdom, and it is deeply inherent in this body/mind organism we call the human body. Even though most humans are well in advance of the lower animals, this level of instinctual thinking is firmly embedded within us, and will dominate our thinking, emotions and behaviour unless we outgrow it. In addition, its style is coloured by all our past experiences.

Every impression that has come into our memory, be it positive or negative, experiences of love or hate, serenity or fear, accomplishment or failure, joy or dejection, pride or disgrace, acceptance or rejection, success or failure, has left its mark. And this collection of countless millions of impressions (called *samskaras* in yoga) colours every perception we experience, how we think about it, any emotions that result, and what we decide to do about it. The practices of yoga are designed to allow us to become aware of these impressions and our responses to them. In this way our thought responses become much more positive and help us to lead a more enjoyable and productive life.

OTHER THINKING PATTERNS

We have discussed the instinctual mind of the human being and its responses to gross and subtle inputs, but we have other thinking patterns too. We should investigate how they affect the state of our lives, and what we can do about them.

1. Mental rumination

The word 'rumination' comes from the way a cow eats. The food doesn't just go straight down as it does with us, it is stored in a primary stomach called a rumen. From there the cow regurgitates it into the mouth, re-chews it for a while, swallows it again, regurgitates and chews it again, and so on. This is exactly what people do with thoughts. We bring up all the old hurts and resentments: "I should have done this", "He shouldn't have done that", "I should have said this to her", etc. The thoughts may even be happy ones about good times we had, but in many people they are likely to be negative, the process called 'worrying'. Not only is this a waste of time and a cause of stress, it also intensifies the original painful impression and makes it worse. It is as if that thought makes a groove in our mind, and every time we regurgitate it and 'chew on it', the groove becomes deeper, so the negative thought becomes more fixed. These 'grooved' thinking patterns are called *vasanas* in yoga. We must learn ways of *observing* and *interrupting* this *internal monologue*, and one of the main functions of the yoga practices is just this.

2. Habitual thinking patterns

We don't realize it, but each of us has styles of thinking that have become automatic. They are so 'natural' that we hold them to be the normal way of thinking. They lead us into trouble over and over again, but we never think to question them. Possibly the greatest of these trouble makers are thoughts of revenge. Plain common sense (which is not so 'common' by the way) would tell us that if we strike back at a perceived insult from another person, they will then strike back at us, so the whole vendetta blows out of proportion and everybody loses. If we can identify those thoughts of revenge, bigotry, contempt, etc., and replace them with common sense, we are likely to ignore the thing and end it there. The yoga practice of thought observation *(Antar Mouna)* teaches us to become aware of our thought patterns, and to discard the useless ones.

3. Fixed opinions, convictions and attitudes

As our thinking patterns develop over the years, our experiences – positive or negative – cause us to develop certain ways of looking at our life and thinking about what we 'see'. Some of these observations are about ourselves, other people, the world around us, the possible existence of an ultimate consciousness, the reason for life, death, sickness, etc. After a while we reach conclusions and they become firmly embedded in our reasoning. These are our *opinions*. They are based on our own variable experience, and the opinions of other people who have influenced us.

Our opinions might be right or wrong, they may help us or harm us, they may conform to general opinion or they may be quite divergent. But one thing is true. When they form as full-fledged opinions, we can become so attached to them that we believe them to be true. We then call them 'convictions'. Even if they cause us all sorts of trouble, we stick to them like a fly in glue, and may be heard to say what we hear so often: "That's my opinion, and I'm sticking to it."

Yoga helps us to develop the 'witness position' – the ability to stand back and get a new view of events, situations and even our own thought patterns. Then we can question the real truth of all our valued opinions and decide whether we should keep them or not.

Another experience that helps us to challenge our precious opinions is to live in another culture, where the people see life differently and have opinions very different from ours, but equally valid. As a matter of fact, cultural shock, that discomfort we feel at first living in cultures different from our own, is partly due to our over-valued opinions being challenged.

When opinions take on an emotional tone we often call them 'attitudes'. Then they become "I like that" or "I don't like that", and this often leads to actions – some beneficial for all involved but some most inappropriate. Often it is not events that hurt us but our attitudes towards them. Yoga recommends, as a counter to such problems, the trio of acceptance, non-expectation of outcomes and equanimity.

77

Acceptance
- See things as they really are; don't resent them because they are not as you want, or waste time fantasizing that they are better. See events and people realistically – one thing in your power is your attitude towards them – either accept them (and get on with life) or reject them.

Non-expectation of outcomes
- "Contentment and fulfilment begin with a clear understanding of one principle – some things are within our control and some are not." (Epictitus, Stoic philosopher of Ancient Greece)
- "Don't worry about anything you cannot change."
- "Lord, grant me the serenity to accept the things I cannot change, the courage to change the things I can, and the wisdom to know the difference." (The Serenity Prayer by Reinhold Neibuhr, a 19th century American clergyman)

Equanimity
- Develop the ability to accept the ups and downs of life as they are. Swami Satyananda said, "Life is full of ups and downs, but for the yogi every 'up' is a joy and every 'down' is an adventure."
- "There is no such thing as a problem without a gift in its hand for you. You seek problems because you need their gifts." (Richard Bach[2])
- "Only a saint prays for problems."

4. Biases, bigotry etc.

These are not just opinions that we believe are true; we *know* they are true even though they are wrong, and they can be very destructive. They are usually the domain of people with poor thinking ability, who are unable to see other points of view. Their thinking is limited to simple fundamentals and concrete concepts, and because they are not capable of seeing 'the bigger picture', they can't understand any reasoning and viewpoints to the contrary. It is a tamasic level of reasoning.

Interestingly, some quite intelligent people are also caught in this trap. They seem to have 'holes' in their intelligence which allow their generalizations and bigotry about ethnic groups, colour, gender and race to exist side by side with efficient thinking. It is said that 'love is blind', but often 'hate is blind' too. These people often benefit by doing the yoga practices (usually they take it up for another reason). Yoga loosens up their convictions, and at the same time they mix with broadminded and tolerant people. A yoga ashram is good for this.

Levels of higher mind

The main way we interact with our world at the more human level is as follows:

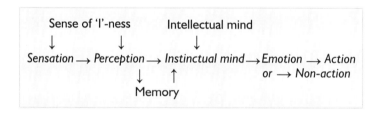

1. Intellectual mind (buddhi)

So far we have been discussing mental functions driven by the instinctual mind which are still a powerful part of our makeup, but we humans are capable of better quality thinking than that. Overseeing these instinctual processes is the intellectual mind. In some people it is poorly developed, and they are still fairly much instinctual beings, but the average person nowadays has it functioning at the level of rational thinking and general common sense. As we know, some of the more evolved of the race have a high degree of thinking power, with an accompanying level of ethics and aspiration for the good of all. However, this is still in the realm of rational thinking where we try to know something by manipulating facts (if we have them) to reach appropriate conclusions. Higher than this again is intuition.

2. Intuition

This is the process of just knowing. It is not a thinking process; it is information from a higher level of our being that gives us the correct viewpoint of situations, correct ideas, and guides our way to correct understanding and decisions. It is the very basis of wisdom, that ability to know the best course of action to take in any situation. Even higher than intuition is the vast realization of the *enlightenment experience* – the very culmination of yoga. So our potential way of interacting with the world at this level includes those given in the diagram.

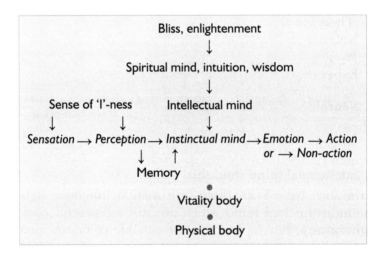

EMOTIONS

These are the personal feeling states such as joy, sadness, fear, love, anger, etc., that are aroused in the individual in response to perceptions, thinking, fantasy and memory. They can be aroused by definite thought processes, or they can appear to come 'out of the blue' from the memory.

However, it is interesting how often we can detect, if we try, the subliminal thoughts or experiences that have triggered an apparently spontaneous emotion. Once I was sitting in a train at a station in India and had a sudden feeling of excitement, just like a delighted little boy. It apparently came from nowhere. When I looked around, I saw another train, which I hadn't noticed, painted in blue and white, looking exactly like the Caves Express train that used to take our family on holidays from Sydney to the mountains when I was that delighted little boy. This can happen with negative emotions too. When I was practising psychiatry, many of my Vietnam War veteran patients re-experienced the horror of the war before they *consciously* heard the sound of the approaching helicopter that had triggered the emotional experience.

There are mainly three components to emotion:
1. Neurological
2. Physiological and expressive
3. Experiencing emotion

1. Neurological components of emotion

These are generated in the brain, and occur at two levels:

a) Sub-cortical emotional responses from the *lower* levels. These occur automatically, suddenly and quickly mainly in the area of the limbic system in the mid-brain – the so-called 'mammalian brain'. They especially defend the individual against harm by creating a sudden action of fight or avoidance. This is the usual source of spontaneous emotions.

b) Cortical responses, which use the *higher* centres of the neo-cortex – the modern, human part of the brain. These create a more advanced quality of the emotions for use in more complex situations and subtler inter-personal relation-ships. One important advantage we receive from yoga is that the 'witness position' gives us the ability to observe what is going on, without becoming emotionally entangled in it. The neo-cortex is an important level through which this works.

2. Physiological and expressive components of emotion

a) The *physiological* components of emotion have for many years been identified as the autonomic nervous system and the endocrine glands. They prepare the body to respond in the appropriate way to the emotion, and thus deal with the event that triggered the emotion. An example is the 'fight or flight' mechanism that uses adrenalin and the sympathetic nervous system to prepare the body to cope with a fear-arousing situation. There are probably similar responses to all the other emotions, including the positive ones; no doubt we will discover them in time, such as the chemistry of love. More recent research has also discovered a whole range of other neurochemicals, called peptides, which form an emotion-based information network linking every part of the body, including the brain and the immune system.

b) The *expressive* components are the expressions of emotion and their counterparts in our posture. They express themselves especially through the facial muscles, such as smiling or looking angry or frightened, and their function seems to be to signal our emotion to other individuals. Humans are 'smarter' – we can use the reasoning power of our neo-cortex to feign false expressions. But we don't really get away with it, because other aspects of our posture and body language usually give us away. Our smell also gives away the truth of our emotions to animals, and maybe even (unconsciously) to humans. The emotion of our prevailing temperament also determines our *posture*. We can easily identify the stooped posture of the depressed person even if they are smiling, or the closed posture of the person under threat even if they are trying to look brave, or the open expansive posture of the confident person even if they are trying to look modest. The yoga asanas deal with postural problems, and often release emotions at the same time.

3. Experiencing emotion

This is the aspect of our emotions and feelings with which we are most familiar – the way we feel – joyous, angry, calm, frightened, loving, and all the others so well known to us. Why do we get them? What function do they serve? They are the power that motivates us to act – their function is to 'push us into' behaviour that is appropriate to cope with the event or situation that caused the emotion. In the untrained animal this usually happens automatically, but in the human, the neo-cortex in the brain can override this automatic response to make us behave in a better way, or not act at all. But we may pay a price for this – the blocked emotion may become repressed into our unconscious mind and cause trouble for the rest of our life. In addition, the blocked action may become 'frozen' into our posture and cause us physical difficulties. Yoga has practices for opening up our mind and our posture and discharging the emotion, freeing us for ever.

Conscious thinking and feeling

As we know, each of us has developed different ways of thinking and feeling about the situations going on around us. Funnily enough, we often believe that other people naturally think and feel the way we do, but that is not true. Each of us sees our world in a unique way; we reason about it differently, and those thoughts cause different emotions in us. For instance, some people love to jump out of aeroplanes at 10,000 feet and hope that a parachute will open so that they don't go down the fast way! They *perceive* the whole thing as positive, they *think* it is a good idea, and they *feel* pleasantly exhilarated when it is happening. I suspect that most of us would not share their enthusiasm.

In the same way, these differences in perceiving our world, thinking about it and feeling about it will define whether we have positive or negative experiences with the situations it presents to us. Yoga teaches us the awareness and witnessing techniques to examine our different responses and their causes, and allows us to learn to lower our stress levels as well.

In the human, behaviour can vary anywhere from physical actions or verbal responses to subliminal body language and even telepathic communication. At some level of perception other people (and animals) can detect even those subtle behaviours, so we are communicating with them at many levels. Usually our responses are appropriate to the situation, and a person can trace a sensible line through the natural perception of an event, logical thinking about it, predictable emotions and the appropriate behaviour. However, traces of old experiences down in our memory stores can give us enduring attitudes, opinions and *habitual behaviour responses* that are certainly not appropriate. These can cause us and other people a lot of trouble.

Habitual responses

Sometimes we hear a person say such things as, "He insulted me, so of course I hit him," or, "She criticized me, so of course I was deeply hurt," or, "He walked past and ignored me, so of course then I was worried about what I had done to him." Can you see what all these have in common?

Firstly, the person could have responded in many other ways to those situations. For example, we can respond to an insult in ways other than hitting the person – we could insult back as most people do, or we could simply say, "Why did you say that?" Or just smile. Similarly, we can respond to a criticism in many ways, the best being to calmly assess the accuracy of the criticism, and then if it is actually appropriate, apologize or take some other remedial action, and vow to ourselves not to do it again. In the same way, if a friend ignores us in the street, we could entertain the possibility that the person who walked past had left his spectacles at home and didn't even see us. Life is full of such situations where we have to assess reasons for occurrences and respond to them, but we often respond to them in a habitual and incorrect way. Yoga helps us to objectively observe our responses, and if we detect a habitual negative response, reason with it and eliminate it.

Secondly, but importantly, notice the words, *"of course"*. As soon as we hear those words, we know we have heard one of the old habitual responses. If we 'hear' the, "of course" in ourselves (even in our thoughts) or in a person we are helping, we should question it immediately. Those responses are often wrong, and are causing trouble in the person's life. The principles and practices of yoga teach us to recognize our destructive responses and to get rid of them.

OTHER REASONS WE ARE SO DIFFERENT?

We all perceive, we all think, we all have emotions and we all behave in one way or another. And our memories are an important factor in determining what we will do in each of these aspects of our experience. However, as well as all our individual differences, because of the *content* within each of these areas we also differ from each other by the *amount that we 'specialize' in one or other of them.*

The thinkers
Some people stay fairly much in their thoughts. They will do a lot of thinking about their situation, and the thinking continues, often without the process continuing on to stages of *emotions* and *behaviour.* Thinkers can usually be shaken out of their cogitations if the situation is important enough to need emotions and actions, but generally they go through life just contemplating and analyzing what is going on. These people are always asking questions, and will pursue a subject until they have all the answers they want. They pursue knowledge, and the commonest word they use is 'why?' Some who are really 'caught up' in their thoughts ruminate about a subject or a situation so much that they are too busy thinking about it to actually *do* anything about it.

Thinkers really need to participate in the wide range of yoga to balance themselves, but they most easily take to *jnana yoga* – the yoga of contemplation and realization.

The feelers

These people are more emotional in nature. They will often respond emotionally to a situation without thinking very much about it, and this can be pleasant for them if the emotions are those of love, joy, positivity about life, intimacy with another person, compassion, etc. However, they suffer a lot if the emotions are negative ones such as insecurity, fear, sadness, hate, etc. It is these people who frequently find themselves in a state of emotion without there being any apparent cause for it; it just seems to 'bubble up from deep down'. The feelers especially need the yoga techniques that balance their body/mind, and they are natural practitioners of *bhakti yoga* – the yoga of devotion and service to humankind. Bhakti gradually converts the negative feelings into positive ones, and stabilizes their lives in a very constructive way.

The action types

These people are the 'get-up-and-go' types. They are dynamic in their lifestyle, and jump in and do things while others are still thinking about it or worrying about the consequences. It is good to have these people involved in any undertaking because they will start the action and make it easy for others to follow and help complete the job. Often, however, they act without first thinking about the consequences or assessing the effects on the other people in the team. They also frequently have a lot of ego involved, and tend to 'own' jobs in which they are involved. These people should take the time to digest what *karma yoga* – meditative selfless service – is all about, because that is their natural path in yoga, and through it they develop concentration, non-ego involvement, objectivity and a positive compassionate outlook.

The daydreamers

Daydreamers are much closer to their unconscious mind than to the events of the outside world. Their perceptions of the world lead them into their memories, and they tend to get stuck there. This makes them rather impractical on the usual level, and other people call them 'flaky' or 'dreamer'. The action types, especially, become frustrated by their life of reverie. However, these people should not be dismissed so readily, because their easy access to the non-logical levels of mind, such as intuition and extrasensory perceptions, make them valuable team mates if the others appreciate and act on their guidance. The daydreamers take easily to the meditation practices and develop well with *raja yoga*; they are doing it naturally anyway. However, when they are not doing 'eyes-closed' meditation, they should keep their eyes and awareness well and truly open in karma yoga to balance the other sides of their nature.

The observers

These people hardly go beyond the stage of perception. They witness the events of life without being very affected by their memories of similar events, without forming value judgements about what is going on, without becoming emotional about them, and without being motivated to do anything about them. Many people are just like this naturally, and in some ways it is akin to the 'witness' state we try to develop in yoga. This is an extremely valuable ability to have because if we choose, we can avoid getting caught up in all the 'dramas' around us, and the vast majority of situations that worry people are just that – 'dramas'.

If we are the witness, we can mentally stand back and assess a situation instead of being dragged into it. In this way we are more able to do something useful. Many people worry that the witness position makes us uncaring, that we will not help other individuals in trouble. It is just the opposite. It makes us more able to help other people because our decisions and actions are not encumbered by a whole lot of negative emotions, taken in from the situation.

Another concern is that we may be so objective that we fail to notice situations that actually are important to us, but in the true witness position, which is 'above' the situation, this doesn't happen either. Remember that this witness position is not from an attitude of apathy, but from a higher perspective – we are above the 'field of battle' as it were, observing the whole scene and assessing events. Actually, ignoring problems is a neurotic response of *denial* of the person who is *too* caught up in the dramas of life.

Awareness

What are we trying to do in this yogic activity of controlling the mind and its related functions? Simply to become aware of it, know it and know when to stop it from running away with us. The beginning of this is to *learn* what the mind is all about, its tricks and its ability to make you think that *it* is *you*. This is what we have discussed in this section of the book.

The next thing to do is *become aware* of the movements of the mind, and we do this through the practices of yoga, which are listed in the section 'Yoga Techniques for Evolvement'.

We learn to become the aware witness. As St Francis of Assisi said: "That which is looking is what you are looking for." Let's keep looking.

A Yogic View of
Personality and its
Evolvement

7

Personality and the Aspects of the Chakra Systems

The term *chakra system* means all the different components of the person that are associated with a particular chakra. When we are thinking about the chakras, we should consider each one as an actual chakra *system,* and realize that all the different components of each system act together. The system consists of the related parts of the body, the energy system, the lower mental and emotional components, the higher mental and feeling components, and the highest realization of those aspects of the individual.

So a chakra system involves all these components, and we will use it as our model when we deal with each individual chakra.

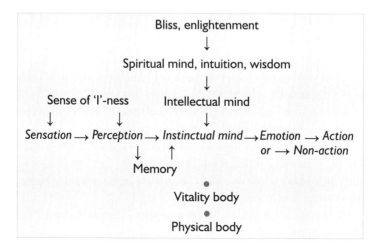

Bliss, enlightenment
↓
Spiritual mind, intuition, wisdom
↓
Sense of 'I'-ness Intellectual mind
↓   ↓   ↓
Sensation → Perception → Instinctual mind → Emotion → Action
↓   ↑   or → Non-action
Memory
•
Vitality body
•
Physical body

The following is a list of some of the relevant qualities of the chakras.

MOOLADHARA

Basic qualities: Security of the individual and material possessions. Some say that as well as self-preservation, this chakra is concerned also with the preservation of the species, so it involves the reproductive role of sexuality.

Physical: The legs, feet and lower bowel. The nerve plexus is the coccygeal plexus, and the endocrines are the adrenal glands (involved in the fear/flight response) and the gonads (reproductive aspect).

Vitality: Mooladhara is the seat of *kundalini shakti,* an energy force which can rise up sushumna nadi and awaken all the potentials of the chakras.

'I'-ness: The sense of identity at this chakra (as in the others) depends on the level of one's evolvement of these qualities. In mooladhara it can vary anywhere from the lowest level of terrified obsession with survival in tamas, through strong ego in rajas, to oneness with the highest consciousness in sattwa.

Perception: At this chakra one sees the world in terms of safety, physical survival and material security. One is also concerned with the security of one's position in 'the bosom' of society.

Memory: Activate mooladhara chakra and up come memories of past experiences of security or insecurity, material gains or losses, etc.

Instinctual mind: Thoughts are concerned with immediate security and getting and conserving possessions.

Intellectual mind: Plans for ensuring one's future security. This may involve bodily or family safety, but is frequently about material security such as position in society, money, property and other possessions.

Higher mind: Planning to ensure one's ability to contribute to the benefit of all.

Emotions and feelings: Depending on one's level will vary through fear, insecurity, greed, acquisition, security, generosity, unity, etc.

Actions: Will usually be related to the thinking and emotional levels.

SWADHISTHANA

Basic qualities: Joy, humour, sexuality.

Physical: Lower part of the trunk, especially the lumbo-sacral area of the spine, pelvic area, buttocks and the genitals. The nerve plexus is the sacral plexus and the endocrines are the gonads (related to the pleasure aspect of sexuality).

Vitality: Sexual energy.

'I'-ness: One's sense of identity at this chakra is of an emotional, feeling, sexual and pleasure seeking individual, who is either fulfilled or frustrated, and the following aspects will depend on which of these applies. Sexual identity in most people corresponds with their gender.

Perception: One sees the world as the potential supplier of pleasure, joy, ecstatic sensations and intimacy, not even suspecting that these are all within one, just waiting to be experienced.

Memory: Activate swadhisthana chakra and the memories that come up out of the unconscious mind will be those of past pleasures and frustrations, sexual experiences, joys and disappointments.

Instinctual mind: Seeks pleasure at all costs – must be careful of inadvisable exploits and addictions.

Intellectual mind: The keys here are sensible restraint of the satisfaction of desire states, and how to sublimate some of the energy of the desires into useful accomplishments.

Higher mind: The realization that the pleasure we seek 'out there' is already the bliss 'in here.'

Emotions and feelings: Anything from depression and guilt to divine ecstasy.

Actions: Will vary in quality according to the above.

MANIPURA

Basic qualities: Power, action, self-esteem.

Physical: Middle part of the trunk, especially the thoraco-lumbar area; digestive system, especially stomach, liver, gall bladder, pancreas and spleen. The nerve plexus is the solar plexus, and the endocrines are the adrenals (involved in the 'fight for food' response) and the pancreas islets (involved in energy supply).

Vitality: Manipura is the centre of pranic energy in the individual.

'I'-ness: This is the centre of *ego*; there can be a strong sense of self as superior or inferior to others.

Perception: The person who is strongly identified here sees power everywhere, and assesses the people and situations around as to who is powerful and who is powerless.

Memory: Activate manipura and the memories will be about past experiences of power, powerlessness, anger, confidence, self-esteem, shame, success, failure, etc.

Instinctual mind: Power, control, will and action are the main thinking patterns at this level.

Intellectual mind: Subtle power becomes obvious at this point; one realizes that one can get things done better by not pressuring or bullying people.

Higher mind: Vast power and miracles are possible at this level, when the person realizes, "It's not me doing all this after all – there is a higher force moving the 'pieces' on the 'board'."

Emotions and feelings: At ordinary levels may vary through pride, shame, self-satisfaction, egotism, anger, etc.

Actions: Will depend on the level of one's evolvement, but may vary through lethargic inactivity, 'pushy' bullying, all the way to pure service of humanity in partnership with divine grace.

ANAHATA

Basic qualities: Love, compassion.

Physical: Thoracic area, including heart, lungs and breasts, and parts of the shoulders and arms. The nerve plexus is the cardiac plexus. The endocrines are the prolactin secretions of the pituitary (the nurturing and breast developing hormone), and the thymus gland and lymph nodes (of the immune system).

Vitality: The *shakti* (vitality) of love.

'I'-ness: Identification at this chakra perceives oneself as a truly social being in relationship with others.

Perception: Looking out at the world through anahata chakra, one sees relationships, possibilities for giving and receiving love, and opportunities for helping. Because of the compassionate nature of this chakra, the person may also selectively perceive all the suffering around and this can cause them a lot of distress.

Memory: The memories here will be of loving, hating and lost intimacies. The old hurts at this chakra can be so painful that we usually don't want to re-visit them; but we must if we are to become fully loving ourselves.

Instinctual mind: At this level our thinking is: "How can I get this person to give me love?"

Intellectual mind: The thinking process at this level is the realization that we have to give love to receive it in return.

Higher mind: There is no thinking about love at this level, there is no need to; the love just flows out to everyone, asking nothing in return.

Emotions and feelings: Love and compassion are the feelings, but the opposite emotions can very easily pour forth if one's conditional love doesn't have all its conditions fulfilled.

Actions: Approaching the loved one with warmth is the automatic action of the heart.

VISHUDDHI

Basic qualities: Communication, purification.

Physical: Throat, larynx, oesophagus, neck area in general, upper arms. The nerve plexuses are the cervical and brachial plexuses, and the endocrines are the thyroid gland (metabolic function) and the parathyroids (calcium metabolism).

Vitality: The energy of communication, charisma.

'I'-ness: One identifies oneself as a person in relationship with others, and (hopefully) realizes that good communication is also good listening.

Perception: The world is seen as a place where there are others with whom to communicate.

Memory: Usually memories of positive communication, or difficulties such as being laughed at, etc.

Instinctual mind: Simple communication with the family or group.

Intellectual mind: Self-expression, creativity, language, words, musical ability, melody, rhythm, etc. Purification, also an aspect of this chakra, clears the way for truer more accurate and honest communication.

Higher mind: Communication with the highest level of consciousness.

Emotions and feelings: May vary from exhilaration at one's fluency to embarrassment at one's difficulty communicating.

Actions: This includes all acts of communication and creativity – speaking, music, rhythm, body language, expression of feelings, even mental telepathy. We communicate with each other on gross and subtle levels.

AJNA

Basic qualities: Intellect, intuition, wisdom, psychic abilities.

Physical: Located in the centre of the brain, related to the central nervous system in general, sight and insight in particular. The endocrine gland is the pineal gland which secretes the 'peace of mind' hormone melatonin, and the 'mind opening' hormone pinoline. Responsible, in unison with the hypothalamus, for the sleep/waking cycle.

Vitality: The confluence of ida, pingala, sushumna – where the main nadis join.

'I'-ness: The person identified at this chakra is usually the unemotional thinker.

Perception: Can be at all levels, including extrasensory perception such as receiving thoughts, clairvoyance, precognition, etc.

Instinctual mind: Ordinary thinking level.

Intellectual mind: Higher intellect.

Higher mind: Intuition, wisdom.

Actions: Usually follow thoughts.

A few things to remember

1. One of the components of each chakra system is its memory stores of past experiences. For each chakra they are the memories of experiences that are associated with the different qualities of that system. For instance, old experiences concerning one's personal security are in the memory stores that connect directly with mooladhara chakra; those to do with sexuality with the swadhisthana system, etc.

2. If a chakra system is activated, a response will occur at all levels of that chakra system; in our memory, perceptions, thinking patterns, emotions and our tendency to behave in a certain way.

3. How are the chakras activated? Outside occurrences and reminders coming in through the sensory system are the commonest activators. For instance, external threats to one's security or reassurances about it will activate the mooladhara chakra system. Sometimes we don't even notice the stimulus; smells, sounds in the background, or sights out of the corner of one's eye are common triggers. Or we may think ourselves into it with the mental ruminations of

the internal monologue – how many people have fantasized themselves into fear, or anger, or a sexual experience?

Sometimes emotions or feelings can just well up out of the unconscious mind unprovoked, and start us having the other experiences of that chakra system. Maybe even cosmic events such as the phases of the moon can do it, as we will mention in Chapter 9.

4. Because activation occurs in all components of the system, circumstances of our lives will reflect themselves in our physical wellbeing, our various kinds of vitality, and through the mental levels shown in the diagram on page 91. We can see this happen spontaneously when emotional stress within the area of security leads to physical illness associated with mooladhara chakra, such as diarrhoea, or sexual problems and conflicts may cause lower back problems and troubles in the sexual organs. In the same way, threats to our power and control can cause problems in the digestive tract, emotional hurts can lead to heart problems, and communication difficulties may lead to neck troubles, laryngitis and thyroid problems.

5. In yoga we can reverse this, using physical and other practices to activate the chakra systems, to bring up the unconscious memories associated with the problems, and to deal with these in our meditation practices.

6. The principles of the chakra systems give us a whole new way of looking at illness, especially obvious psycho-somatic illness (which is most of it), and a clear lead into assessing the causes and management of illnesses. It shows us where we can intervene with yoga in the stress process, hopefully before the stress causes damage to the body's tissues and organs.

7. Remember though, that in general yoga does not specialize in activating only one chakra system. We try to balance the effects on all the chakras, doing practices for one, then another, then another, so that in any yoga session, all the chakra systems have been activated. Then we do a meditation practice and see what comes up.

The unity of the systems

Remember that even though we are dividing these systems into their chakra groups, they are not separate; they are intercommunicating all the time. At the physical level there is certainly communication throughout the whole body, not just via the nerves and hormones, but also each part of the body is continuously in contact with every other part by a complex system of communication peptide molecules, such as the endorphins. If there is trouble in one of the chakra systems, all the others will 'know about it' and be influenced by it. Similarly, if we can eliminate a problem in one of the chakra circuits or evolve the qualities associated with it, the benefits will flow through to the others.

The yogis do not perceive these things we are discussing as being separate parts; in fact they see the whole body/energy/mind complex of all the chakra circuits as being one. To get the gist of yogic understanding, it is always necessary to think in terms of the unity which each chakra system is just a part of and the unity of the different components of each system. Then we use our yoga practices holistically, attending to all the chakra systems, and working on each of the different components of each system.

Evolvement of these qualities

In this chapter we have looked at the different aspects of the personality as they relate to the chakra systems, and to the various manifestations of those in the person. Now we will look at the way the gunas – sattwa, rajas and tamas – can describe the different levels of evolvement of these in any person. This perspective will then serve as a basis on which we can build the rest of this yogic personality model, and show us how we can use the practices of yoga to evolve ourselves.

8

Evolvement of the Aspects of the Personality

Remember:
- Chakras are one way of looking at personality.
- Chakras are real. Satyananda Yoga works with them to evolve our personality.
- Each of us 'specializes' in one or two, and we will deal with this later.
- The most active chakras for each of us helps determine our own personal 'style' of relating to our world.
- The chakra system is not as simple as this, but it is a valid model for looking at our personality.
- Divisions between the levels as described by the gunas are gradual.
- All of us already are the highest levels! How?

We are already enlightened
- For thousands of years, the spiritual adepts have told us, from their enlightened level, that each one of us is already at the highest level of consciousness. But we are caught down in a lower level of awareness, as we identify with the body, the ego and our roles in life.
- All it needs is for us to get out of the lower 'dramas', then we become our real potential.

PERSONALITY, THE CHAKRA ASPECTS AND THE GUNA QUALITIES

The different aspects of the chakras within us are modified by the level of their development as defined by the gunas, so we can assess the effect each one has on the dimensions of our personality. In this way we can envision how they contribute to "our personal style of interacting with our physical and social environments" (remember the definition of personality).

No matter how evolved our six chakra aspects are, they will influence us in the following ways we have been discussing:
· Our *physical* wellbeing
· Our *vitality* – physical and mental
· Our *'I'-ness* – experienced as autonomy, ego, identity and self
· The way we *perceive* our world
· The *memories* associated with each aspect
· *Instinctual mind* – its responses to the perceptions, and its other thoughts
· *Intellectual mind* – the degree to which one can access it, the quality of its thinking, and the ethics of its plans
· *Higher mind* – the degree to which one can access it, and the experiences as a result
· *Emotions* and *feelings* – their quality
· *Actions* – their quality.

Try to keep these personality aspects in mind as we proceed through the chakras.

The gunas and evolvement of chakra aspects

Evolution of the personality aspects associated with the chakras will be discussed at these different guna sub-levels:
· Tamasic
· Tamasic-Rajasic
· Rajasic-Tamasic
· Rajasic
· Rajasic-Sattwic

- Sattwic-Rajasic
- Sattwic
- Enlightened.

MOOLADHARA – SECURITY

Mooladhara – *Tamasic*

This is the level of our lowest sense of personal security. If we are confronted with a dangerous situation, we will almost all react with appropriate fear. But what we are talking about at this most tamasic level of mooladhara is the ongoing state of terror in which some unfortunate people live their lives, usually caused by severe emotional trauma in their past. It can actually become 'hard wired' into their nervous systems, so that it becomes physical and therefore chronic. However, recent scientific evidence has shown that even this can be reversed, because at any age *the brain continually changes physically as a result of our experiences* – whether through new connections between nerve cells or even by creation of completely new nerve cells – a process called *neuro-plasticity.* Some people with post-traumatic stress disorder are stuck in this tamasic level of mooladhara, and have been reliving a terrible traumatic event in nightmares and daytime 'flashbacks' for 60 years or more.

People under the influence of the tamasic level of mooladhara *perceive* the world as a dangerous place, their *thoughts* are of the 'won't it be terrible if', or, 'what if' variety and lead them to be always on their guard – a state called *hypervigilance.* Their ongoing *emotion* is extreme fear or at least just ordinary fear when they are having a 'good' day, and at this level their *behaviour* usually centres on ways to *avoid* any situation that may increase their anxiety. The physical techniques of yoga can help these people if they can rouse themselves out of tamas to practise them, but tamas tends to get people *stuck* where they are. Pratyahara techniques such as Yoga Nidra (a deep mental relaxation practice described later) can help, but it is advisable to use only the mental relaxation level at the beginning, because going down into the memories of the unconscious mind is too painful for these people.

Mooladhara – *Tamasic-Rajasic*
This is the typical anxiety disorder, often with phobic elements, that psychiatrists and psychologists treat on a regular basis. Quite a large number of people who generally function at a higher level will often 'dip down' into this level in response to a life stress, and be socially incapacitated for a while. Then with some help (or maybe alone), they will move back up into rajas or higher, and get on with their lives. In the state of anxiety the person *perceives* possible troubles all around them. They are the typical 'worriers', and their *thought* patterns revolve around anticipating things going wrong and what they hope to do about them. Their *emotion* is fear or at least apprehension, although they may often experience periods during their day when the emotions are calm. They may do quite well with a balanced series of yoga practices, and often form the 'backbone' of many yoga classes in the community. The *behaviour* pattern of these people is not *avoidance* as in tamas, but actively *seeking relief* from their anxiety, as the activating influence of rajas helps to overcome the inertia, avoidance and 'stuck-ness' of tamas.

Mooladhara – *Rajasic-Tamasic*
Because of the stronger rajasic influence, these people have much more drive to do something about their problem. The tamas still holds them in the negative state, but they try to solve the problem by the old mooladhara trick of accumulating money and possessions. They use greed to allay their fear, and may even use dishonest means to get what they want, if they have a low ethical level of the tamasic influence. Can people be quite evolved in one or more chakras and tamasic in others? It is unusual, but nowadays we can cite recent examples of the very clever and powerful senior executives of big companies who, because of their

103

criminal greed (low mooladhara development), have caused the businesses to collapse while they walked off with millions of dollars. The *perception* of people at this rajasic-tamasic level of mooladhara is looking for opportunities to get more money and possessions, often by fair means or foul. The *thought* patterns centre on money and property; in fact when you are with them that may be all they talk about. Confidence tricksters come from this group. The *emotional state* of these people is usually neutral while the money is coming in because their insecurity is hidden under their acquisitiveness; their *behaviour* is directed towards getting more and more. The big fear that lurks below, of course, is of 'losing it all' and being exposed to that terrible unknown! During the Great Depression in the late 1920s many men jumped out of multi-story buildings in this state of mind.

Mooladhara – *Rajasic*

These people take care of their security in a direct manner. Their actions are much more balanced and inclusive than those who are afflicted by tamas. They are acquisitive for personal gain, but rather than hoarding money and possessions, they will use it to ensure other areas of their security such as relationships with other people. They also sense the other aspect of mooladhara chakra – the security of the species – by producing and nurturing children. They don't neglect their families in the headlong pursuit of wealth as the rajasic-tamasic people may do. Rather, they include the family, and even friends, in their activities and at this level they can be very good providers for their family, making money for housing, food, clothing, education, etc. These people *perceive* their world as an area of opportunity. Their *thoughts* are oriented towards sensible and honest money-making, accumulation of property and providing for the family. Their *emotions* about security are neutral, as long as things are going OK, and their *behaviour* is directed towards sensibly, but selfishly, acquiring money and necessary possessions.

Mooladhara – *Rajasic-Sattwic*

When the sattwa starts to shine on any aspect of our personality, we start to experience the 'bigger picture'. We realize that *generosity* is also a way of providing for our security, an idea that would seem ridiculous to people at the lower levels. At this level the generosity is still very much a 'me' oriented activity – "I'll scratch your back if you scratch mine" – but it is a good start. These people contrive to secure their security, acquire possessions and provide for the family by including *conditional generosity* in their dealings with other people. They will make mutually beneficial agreements, so that both sides of the deal will win. Their *perception* of the world in this aspect of their personality is of identifying such opportunities, and their *thinking* is along the same lines. The *emotion* is usually one of contentment as long as everything on the money front is going well, they feel pride in the family and self-satisfaction. Their *behaviour* is in line with these.

Mooladhara – *Sattwic-Rajasic*

At this level, generosity is very much in the *nature* of the person, rather than a means of opportunity as in the previous group. The person realizes that material possessions are not really a source of inner security. Rather they can be a source of insecurity because of the fear of losing them, unless we have an unattached attitude. Such people are starting to realize that as long as our basic needs are satisfied, security is an internal quality, not related to how much we have. They see that mega-rich people can still feel insecure as they desperately struggle for more and more, while people living a simple life can be contented. As the old saying goes: "Wealth is not having a lot, but being content with what we have." Accordingly, these people do obtain and maintain possessions, but they use them for good work while they lead a simple life. Their *perception* is of looking to get the possessions required for their work, their *thinking* is of what is needed, and their *emotion* is of contentment and satisfaction with their financial position. Their *behaviour* is to accumulate what they need and use the rest for the benefit of others.

Mooladhara – *Sattwic*

People at this level of mooladhara functioning just *are* security, they have it as a 'gut feeling'. They are still aware that the body is vulnerable to harm, and that it has needs of nutrition, shelter and protection, but if those are supplied, security is automatic. By this level they have also had so many experiences of *divine grace* in their lives, they now realize that as long as each one of us is 'travelling' on his or her right individual path (called *swadharma* in yoga), security is ours. To people who have not noticed these experiences of divine grace, this whole idea seems absurd. But it is an accepted part of life for someone who has noticed all those apparent 'coincidences' one after the other, sometimes ten times in the one day – too frequent to be just coincidences. Things fall into place just as they need to, or the right person to do the job appears at just the right time, or the unavoidable mess-up in arrangements leads to the right outcome, or the right amount of money needed for the job just 'comes along'. More and more we come to realize that real security is a quality of the universe, not of our little human endeavours – and that is a sattwic point of view. Still, If you haven't become aware of divine grace yet, you won't believe it – if you have, I don't need to tell you.

Mooladhara – *Enlightened*

This indescribable experience of the unity of all and our place in the whole is the culmination of our journey to absolute security. To realize our oneness with the absolute and have the very deep feeling that 'everything is all right, it is all going as it should' – that is total security.

How important will these be in our life?

The strength of expression of the mooladhara functions in each of us will determine how important they will be in our life. This applies to each of the chakra systems. We will discuss the effects of dominant chakra aspects on the personality in the next chapter.

If the mooladhara functions are the most powerful aspects of one's personality, the patterns mentioned above will dominate one's life and become a major aspect of the personality.

If other aspects predominate, then those other aspects will form the main substrata of one's perceptions, thoughts, emotions, behaviour, etc. In that case the security-possessions aspect we have just discussed will only move the person from time to time when stimulated. Irrespective of that, however, when they are active, they will express themselves in the ways described above.

SWADHISTHANA – JOY, SEXUALITY

Swadhisthana – *Tamasic*

Extreme sadness and lack of the ability to enjoy life are the cardinal *emotions* at this level. As the person looks around, all they can *perceive* are negative aspects of life. As they *think* back, all the memories are sad ones. As they look forward, all they feel is pessimism and maybe even hopelessness. Because of this they are likely to feel suicidal – as indeed can occur at the bottom level of any of the chakra qualities. These people must have medical help, at least with antidepressant medication, which can be lifesaving. Major depression often develops on this substrata as it floods over into the other chakra areas, and can include also the following:

Emotions
- Low self-esteem, self-depreciation
- Inappropriate guilt is often a problem.

Thinking
- Thinking is slow
- Motivation is low

- Insomnia is common, especially waking early in the morning feeling very depressed
- Pessimism – in the extreme, if the future looks hopeless, suicide is possible
- Fluctuation during the day, usually worst in the morning.

Body
- Vitality is low
- Actions are slow
- Muscles are loose, tense or agitated
- Appetite is usually poor
- Weight loss follows poor appetite
- Constipation is common
- Sexual drive low or non-existent.

This condition, especially if the person is suicidal, can be an acute medical emergency. Remember that people in this condition can gain enormous benefit from modern anti-depressant medication, which is effective and whose side-effect profile is far lower than the threat of suicide – they must have it. After they have stabilized somewhat on medication they can benefit greatly from yoga practices.

Swadhisthana – *Tamasic-Rajasic*

For people at this level of swadhisthana, the main *emotion* is dejection. They are pessimistic, and unable to *perceive* the pleasant side of past, present or future. Addictions can be a real problem in this state. Many unfortunate people spend their whole life in this state of chronic depression; others just sink into it, usually in response to stressful events in their life, and come back out of it when life improves, or when helped by therapy or yoga. Yoga practices can certainly help here, as indeed they can when the people with more severe depression are stabilized on medication. We concentrate on the vitalizing techniques, 'opening' postures, and a small amount of deep mental relaxation (*Yoga Nidra*) using positive affirmations.

Swadhisthana – *Rajasic-Tamasic*

People at this level are more motivated because of the influence of rajas, but because of tamas they still tend to slip into dejected, unhappy, bored and lonely *emotional* states. They try to assuage these by pursuing pleasurable sensations. They may take to overeating, bulimia, alcohol, drugs, gambling, etc. Desire for sex can become an obsession with some, but their sexual adventures are usually just to satisfy their own demand for some pleasure. This usually results in exploitation of the partner, and not much satisfaction for either of them in the end. They can become so sexually preoccupied that all they seem to be able to *perceive* in their world are sexual objects, and they *think* about sex most of the time. These people are also at risk of addiction, bankruptcy (from gambling) and complicated entanglements with sexual partners. It is often these problems that eventually bring them to yoga, and if they can get away from the tempting situations and get their joy from yoga, they can do quite well.

Swadhisthana – *Rajasic*

The positive aspects for people under the influence of rajas, such as positive *emotions*, effort, drive, optimism and flexibility, can make life quite pleasant, as long as things are going their way. They tend to be joy-seeking, they enjoy their sexual life and don't have the troublesome compulsive drive of the rajasic-tamasic person. They often have a good sense of humour, but at this level it can take on an undiplomatic or even hurtful tone. They usually *perceive* their world as being a place of opportunities for fun; they *think* that way and *behave* accordingly when the opportunity presents itself. Their main problem is that of rajas in all the chakra system qualities – the belief that all the good things in life come from 'out there'. At the rajasic level the person hasn't yet realized that the bliss is within, and is not dependent on 'supplies' from other people.

Swadhisthana – *Rajasic-Sattwic*

With sattwa shining down on these people, the swadhisthana qualities take on a more considerate, ethical and compassionate tone. They are kindly, humorous, sexually considerate with love and consideration for the partner, and generally find life pleasant and good fun. But they still have the rajasic quality of always looking for their fulfilment outside themselves, and this still makes them vulnerable. Still, their outward-looking tendency also encourages them to try to make other people happy, so they are usually popular. Their *perceptions* of the world, their *thinking* patterns, their happy *emotions* and their appropriate *behaviour* are usually congruent with the above qualities.

Swadhisthana – *Sattwic-Rajasic*

People at this level have really begun to find the joy within. They are starting to realize that the joy, happiness and pleasure we think we find 'out there' are really just being experienced 'in here' where they have been all the time. As they *perceive* their world, they project their inner joy out there, and see joy all around them, though they attract it too. They are generally happy, contented, humorous and considerate of others. In fact, we may describe them as the 'life of the party', and if their swadhisthana system is well activated, the influence of rajas often keeps these people going to parties and other gatherings regularly.

Swadhisthana – *Sattwic*

These people don't need to experience joy from outside, or to give joy, they just *are* joy. They have a bubbling joy going on inside them all the time. They 'light up' a whole roomful of people just by walking in; they don't have to try to do it. This is an aspect of what people call 'charisma', and why other people love to be with them. They have the natural ability to *perceive* the positive side of everyone and everything, and see the funny side of life. Because they see the positive side, they concentrate on people's potentials

110

for development rather than their 'sins' that 'need to be punished'. They can be wonderful 'life teachers'.

Swadhisthana – *Enlightened*
This is the state of oneness with the total bliss of the ultimate consciousness. This ecstasy has been described by the saints and sages of all spiritual paths. It has been described by some Christian saints as the 'rapture', implying that they felt carried away or transported in bliss into another dimension. To the yogi, it is the result of unblocking and exposing the bliss (*ananda*) that is already us.

MANIPURA – DYNAMIC ACTION, POWER TO ACCOMPLISH, SELF-ESTEEM

Manipura – *Tamasic*
People who are caught up at this level of the manipura quality of *action* are stuck. Some of the characteristics are: inertia, lethargy, laziness, fatigue, dullness, feeling blocked – not a good state to be in if one is trying to act effectively in the world and attain the power to accomplish what needs to be done. These people are not just procrastinators – putting off till tomorrow what they can do today – they don't even do it tomorrow, or the next day either. No wonder they are also low in that other manipura quality – self-esteem. Interestingly, yoga contains many practices to vitalize manipura chakra and get these people moving again, but their apathy – another quality of tamas – may stop them from 'taking the cure'.

Manipura – *Tamasic-Rajasic*
These people are not as apathetic as those at the tamasic level; the rajas gives them the motivation to get going, but the tamas still holds them back. Worse than that, they may even start jobs, but then tamas drags them down again and they leave them incomplete. These people tend to be surrounded by unfinished jobs that clutter up their lives

and cause them increasing distress. Guilt increases and self-esteem decreases as they see all those untidy corners, missed appointments, unanswered letters and, of course, those half-finished jobs. This is a big part of the guilt and low self-esteem suffered by people with major depression. People at this level should try to arrange their lives around small quick jobs, and avoid long ones such as renovating the house, building boats, restoring cars, etc. If they don't, their surroundings are likely to look like a disaster area. They should also learn to say NO to people who want them to do things. They also need the yoga practices that increase physical and mental *vitality*.

Manipura – *Rajasic-Tamasic*

Rajas is stronger in these people, and it may motivate them into action quite well. However, there can be two problems caused by the tamas remaining. Firstly, they can launch whole-heartedly into a task, then right at the end lose interest, and the whole thing (including the interests of other people involved) falls to pieces. They can become very angry over their dissatisfaction, but their pride may prevent them from getting help. The second possible problem involves the impure ethics of tamas, the ignorance of the needs of other people, and negative emotions. In other words, they can exercise power over people in a crude way, so they become bullies and dictators. If their manipura chakra is powerfully activated, and they are intelligent as well, they can be dangerous people indeed. The previous century produced a few such people who rose to positions of great power and destructiveness.

Manipura – *Rajasic*

These people are active and courageous. The vitality of manipura flows well and allows them to accomplish the usual requirements of life. But remember that rajas is also about personal ambition, ego and opportunism, so the activities that are done with such enthusiasm are for Number 1 – me. Such people may help you, but there will usually be a 'percentage' of opportunity of some sort for them. If events force them to work for you without reward, they are likely to stop as soon as you turn your back. Or at least not do the job well. In rajas, negotiations may be done on a competitive win/lose basis – if I can make you lose, I win. (At least this is better than the lose/lose basis of tamas – "I'll smash the toys so that neither of us has them.") The rajasic way of doing things is based on the 'zero sum fallacy' that is the basis of so many competitive sports in which half of the strategy is to stop the other side from scoring. It works well in sports and legal skirmishes, but not in human relationships where win/win solutions are the best. As sattwa starts to shine in a person's life, they begin to look for just these ways in which both sides win. This, of course, requires a sense of concern for the welfare of the other person, honesty, truthfulness, ethics, and patience – ingredients that are in short supply at the lower levels of evolvement.

Manipura – *Rajasic-Sattwic*

The sattwic sense of fairness and consideration for others is starting to shine in the manipura qualities of these people. They are keen and willing to help, willing to do the job to help any cause in which they are involved. These people are the mainstay of church committees, the workers for charity, the volunteers for the school lunch shop, etc. They will work assiduously, without expecting reward, just because they believe in the rightness of the job, the family or the organization in which they are involved.

Manipura – *Sattwic-Rajasic*

'Karma yogis' is the name we give to these people. They function in the world with one-pointed awareness and precision, maintain a positive attitude in success or failure, and have no emotional attachment to receiving rewards (material or personal) for their efforts, or to rewards they do receive. The ego of the rajasic level is overshadowed by sattwa, and they move through the world helping others, and surrounded by grateful friends. At this level another realization dawns: power is simply about getting things done – in physics, power is defined as, 'the ability to do work', and it is the same in our lives – power is our ability to accomplish things. At this level people realize that the 'pushing' power of the lower levels of manipura can limit our ability to get people to do things to help us. If we push too hard, as soon as we turn our backs people may stop, or worse, sabotage the job. Far better is to borrow a little bit of the *love* of anahata chakra. People will work at their very best to help get things done if they love the person who is asking them, or the cause for which they are working. At the sattwic-rajasic level of manipura this becomes automatic, and love becomes a natural part of encouraging people to help us develop a worthy cause.

Manipura – *Sattwic*

"Let go, let God." This is another dimension of action in the world, and it is attained by few people in this era. People at the sattwic level perform their actions for the benefit of others and for the world. But they are aware that they are just an instrument of divine grace. As Swami Sivananda said, "I am the instrument, God is the musician." St Francis said, "Lord, make me an instrument of thy peace." It is our job to put the 'pieces' of the work into place, then we observe with awe and often amusement, the long strings of 'amazing coincidences' as the hand of grace creates all the right conditions and occurrences to make the 'pieces' fall into place to complete the perfect jigsaw. To many people this may seem absurd, but for others it is a matter of experience.

Manipura – *Enlightened*

At this stage one has the realization of the staggering power of the universe. It becomes obvious that the power is not just random, but a coherent scheme of things with a mighty consciousness directing it. Einstein put this well when he said

114

(possibly from the level of his towering intellect rather than the realization of enlightenment):

> Everyone who is seriously in the pursuit of science becomes convinced that a spirit is manifest in the laws of the universe – a spirit vastly superior to that of man, and one in the face of which we with our modest powers must feel humble.

> The scientist's religious feeling takes the form of a rapturous amazement at the harmony of natural law, which reveals an intelligence of such superiority that, compared with it, all the systematic thinking and acting of human beings is an utterly insignificant reflection.

ANAHATA – LOVE

Anahata – *Tamasic*

At this level of anahata the person's concern for others is submerged in the apathy of tamas, and they are emotionally isolated. They have no 'fellow feeling' about the plight or needs of anybody. In fact, if such people are also exploitative, they will use the other individual's vulnerability to their own advantage, and see another person's kindness as stupidity. If they are violent, they are particularly dangerous because of their absence of feeling for other people. The sociopathic personality (often known as the psychopath) is the typical example of this type of person in the community and, not surprisingly, they make up a fair proportion of prison inmates. It is most important that yoga be included in the activities of all prisons throughout the world because it can raise the level of these people and other inmates such as addicts. Research has shown that the teaching of yoga in the prisons of Bihar, India, by Bihar Yoga Bharati has been very successful.

Anahata – *Tamasic-Rajasic*

People at this level of anahata are not as isolated as the tamasic group. They have some affiliations in their own group, which may however be an antisocial group, but they readily betray and exploit each other. They are risky 'friends' to have. Criminal and drug addict groups contain many of these people, and the movie industry has made good 'mileage' out of the dramas of betrayal and counter-betrayal of such people.

Anahata – *Rajasic-Tamasic*

Driven by rajas these people recognize a need for the cooperation of others to fulfil their personal ambitions, ego's desires and opportunism. But when it comes to love and compassion, some of the darkness of tamas is still with them, and usually the best they can muster is false concern, covering the resentment they feel from not being part of the normal group. Because of the stronger rajas though, they can move with the experiences of yoga and change themselves. They may even experience glimmerings of the love of sattwa, and the memories of that can motivate these people to change and improve.

Anahata – *Rajasic*

These people are capable of loving and being loved, but at this level they have not yet become aware of the love that they *are*, so they still believe they need somebody 'out there' to 'give' them love if they are to be fulfilled. So their love is conditional: "I'll love you only if you love me", "promise me you will love me forever", "love only me", etc. It's the stuff of all the 'love' songs from Hollywood, Bollywood and all the other 'woulds'. This may be because the songwriters are themselves still at the level of conditional love, and they are writing the songs for others who are also at this stage. The trouble with 'needing' someone to give you love is, what happens when you turn off the supply? One feels empty, unloved, resentful, angry, maybe even jealous – not very good emotions for a relationship. And this is exactly what is happening in so many relationships in our world today. Such people need to raise their level of awareness to realize their own love within – important areas of yoga give us just this upliftment.

Anahata – *Rajasic-Sattwic*

At this stage people start to experience care for others, compassion, ethics, consideration for the environment and a willingness to help: sattwa releases these qualities within them. At this level they are usually still quite selective about who receives these feelings from them, because the 'me and mine first' influence of rajas is still with them. They care for the family, their pets, close friends, etc., but there is a very important difference from the previous stage – the love they give to their loved ones is unconditional. They *give* it just because they *love* the children, the spouse, the dog, the good friend, etc., and these relationships are starting to become very rewarding indeed.

Anahata – *Sattwic-Rajasic*

At this level that altruistic love and compassion for all, which is so much a part of sattwa, is flooding over from inside into the person's awareness. They see the needs of people and the world as being the concern of all of us, feel joy for those who are in a positive situation, and concern and compassion for those in a more difficult position. They *perceive* the world more clearly and widely, and look for opportunities and *think* of ways to help. Their primary *emotions* are of love and compassion, and their *actions* are directed towards supplying the needs of others as well as themselves. A lot of people who teach and spread the benefits of yoga are among this group.

Anahata – *Sattwic*

The person at this level doesn't just *give* love and compassion, and certainly doesn't need to get it from outside. This person just IS LOVE. They are in a state of love. They have become the love they have always been, the channels for it to express itself are clear, and everyone who

117

comes into their presence can feel it. When they enter a group of other people, any animosity that was in the group just seems to dissolve away. As a result, they go through life seeming to be surrounded by loving people. Of course, as soon as they leave the others may revert back to their old habits, but the 'magic' of someone at this level is that the power of their love is so strong that the people they meet are changed a little bit; they have become a little more loving.

Anahata – *Enlightened*

This is an experience that changes the person forever. To become dissolved in the cosmic love, to become aware that the whole universe is love and compassion for all and everyone gives the person serenity and faith that stays with them long after the enlightenment experience is over. Anxieties and insecurities seem to have dissolved away; there is a deeper love for other people, and a deep realization that 'all is well'. Of course, the body will still have its own built-in fear mechanisms. But the prevailing attitude of the person who has had the experience of cosmic love is one of security, love, compassion, joy and confidence.

VISHUDDHI – COMMUNICATION

Vishuddhi – *Tamasic*

The recluse. The communication of people at this level is blocked. They are isolated, verbally inept and often alienated from those around them. The latter can be a real problem because if we are not communicating with others, it is easy to widen the gap between us, and develop a 'me-they' situation that takes on a suspicious nature and ends with the attitude of the persecuted 'loner'. This is what happens in paranoia, where the alienation becomes so frightening that the breach cannot be healed without physical intervention.

Vishuddhi – *Tamasic-Rajasic*

The wallflower. This person has limited contacts and communication. Often the wife of one of my patients would say, "He doesn't like to go anywhere, Doctor, and even when he does, he just sits there and doesn't say anything." He would often say something like, "What is there to say, Doc, everybody else is doing all the talking." This person is not really isolated like the tamasic person; he is just not adept at conversation. Some of the talkative types might like him this way; they would call him a 'good listener'.

Vishuddhi – *Rajasic-Tamasic*

The complainer. The rajasic component in these people allows the communication to flow, but the tamas can corrupt it with negativity. These people can spend most of their life complaining about everything. Nothing satisfies them, and they let everyone in the vicinity know about it. Almost every positive comment made to them is reversed, and their favourite two words seem to be "Yes but." If you say, "It's a lovely sunny day," they will say, "Yes, but there's a cloud over there."

Vishuddhi – *Rajasic*

The communication in these people flows easily. If vishuddhi chakra is not too charged, they are good conversationalists who enjoy also listening to the opinions of others. They like to relate to other people, but the elements of opportunism and personal ambition inherent in rajas often ensures that they will choose as their conversation partner one who can further their ambitions. If they have a really activated vishuddhi, they can be chatterboxes who dominate every conversation. They need to practise the yoga techniques to balance the chakra activities.

Vishuddhi – *Rajasic-Sattwic*

These people are eloquent. Sattwa lubricates an easy flow of communication, clarity, simplicity and an organized knowledge of a subject. They can take a complicated subject and explain it in a simple meaningful way. They are also, at this stage, developing the rapport that allows them to 'feel' what the other person needs to know, and to incorporate it in an easily understandable way into the conversation or lecture. At this level they have open and free body language too; their whole body communicates with you. In the movie *Zorba the Greek*, Zorba said to a man something like, "You only spoke with your mouth, the rest of your body told me nothing" – he would have approved of communicators at this level.

Vishuddhi – *Sattwic-Rajasic*

At the personal level of communication, the sensitivity, kindness and concern for the welfare of others ensures that any communication is non-hurting – this person is the real diplomat. Added to this is often the ajna quality of being aware, at a psychic level, of other people's needs so that people receive exactly what they need. In group communication and in lectures, the person at this sattwic-rajasic level of vishuddhi develops such a rapport with the audience that he or she seems to unconsciously realize the questions in the minds of the people in the audience, and answer them long before 'question time'. People come up after the lecture and say, "I had a lot questions to ask, but you answered them all in the lecture." Coincidence? Maybe, but it happens so often to some lecturers that the possibility of coincidence becomes very unlikely indeed. This kind of psychic communication occurs in other areas of life as well.

Vishuddhi – *Sattwic*

At this level a new ability opens, and the information is now flowing *through* the person rather than *from* the person. It is information from those higher levels where we are all in touch with each other, and with the higher information, intuition and wisdom. During this kind of communication, we may use information we have derived intellectually, such as principles of anatomy and physiology if one is a physician,

120

but the communication itself is not an intellectual exercise; it is purely intuitive, it just 'flows by itself'. Very few people have experienced this, and most professional teachers will be sceptical, but it is true. Many inspiring lecturers are functioning at this stage, and they do inspire an audience because the people recognize, in some part of their being, that they are hearing the truth. This is also enhanced by the fact that all levels of the communication are congruous – they are all in agreement with each other – the verbal, the body language, the emotions and the psychic levels are all 'saying' the same thing.

Vishuddhi – *Enlightened*

When we move up into this experience, we realize that the whole cosmos is a vast network of communication, and that every word and every thought reverberates throughout the whole. We realize the effect that even a single thought can have on each one of us, and the value of positive and kind thoughts and words in the whole scheme of things. After this experience we become careful with what we say and even what we think.

AJNA – INTELLECT, INTUITION, WISDOM, HIGHER POWERS

Ajna – *Tamasic*

The person at this level has difficulty thinking. They often say, "I can't think," and indeed they have difficulty using logical ways of coming to conclusions. It's not that they are mentally retarded in the true sense of the word, they might be quite intelligent in other qualities of their being, but the tamasic qualities of inertia, lethargy and dullness affect their thinking process.

Ajna – *Tamasic-Rajasic*

The mental processes of these people are more active under the influence of rajas. They can think logically in simple

121

ways, but the tamas keeps tripping them up. Many of them become aware of this and reduce their stress by playing the game of 'Stupid', as it was named by Eric Berne in the 1950s book *Games People Play*. Such people try to appear less intelligent than they are, so that people don't place too many demands on them. They realize that they are vulnerable to messy thinking and being laughed at, so they protect themselves under the guise of 'stupidity' to limit the thinking demands put on them. We are often suddenly taken by surprise by the cleverness of a reply, a witty back answer, or an intelligent conclusion from them.

Ajna – *Rajasic-Tamasic*

The person at this level is a much better thinker, as the movement, effort and energy of rajas move the mind. However, the thinking process may still be clouded by the impurity, 'darkness' and lack of ethics of tamas, and by the ego, selfish ambition and opportunism of rajas. This combination tends to produce sly thinkers, who look for opportunities to attain what they want, and then verbally pressure people into complying with them. Many lower level salesmen are in this category. In the USA, they call them 'snake oil salesmen'.

Ajna – *Rajasic*

People at this level are intellectually competent and logical for everyday requirements. Their thinking processes are still in the service of their own personal desires and ambitions, and those of their family and close friends, but are adequate for their needs. This is the level of the average person who is a competent worker, parent and householder, who has a level of thinking which is the target for most advertising, the daily newspaper and popular magazines.

Ajna – *Rajasic-Sattwic*

These people are considered very intelligent; they think quickly and clearly, and see situations and principles in 'big pictures'. They usually have good memories because they think well enough to assemble concepts into meaningful order for memorizing. They are the people who inhabit the top offices of businesses and government, and the consulting rooms of doctors, lawyers and other professionals. They are attracted to knowledge and education, and they generally live life in a constructive and ethical way. But they also tend to worship the intellect, and this holds them back from advancing further into areas of intuition, real wisdom and higher. Two more quotes from Albert Einstein:

> We should take care not to make the intellect our god; it has, of course, powerful muscles, but no personality.

> The intuitive mind is a sacred gift, and the rational mind is a faithful servant. We have created a society that honours the servant and has forgotten the gift.

Ajna – *Sattwic-Rajasic*

These people are the geniuses. They are creative, original and visionary. Their thinking process is not just logical; it is beyond that, as they are tuning into the information and processes of the higher mind. These higher levels supply them with original concepts and new ways of looking at the world and people. They think 'outside the square', and other people are amazed at their ideas and conclusions.

Ajna – *Sattwic*

These people are in contact with the high levels of mind where they have free access to intuition and wisdom. The conclusions they reach due to this influence are true, and their behaviour based on this is right. In addition they may develop such psychic powers as precognition, telepathy, clairvoyance, healing, etc., but people at this level never use these for personal gain. In fact, they don't use them themselves at all; they just continue to do their work for the benefit of others and the planet, and if these powers appear, they just accept that help in the work.

123

Ajna – *Enlightened*

The person who experiences this level of ajna has the overwhelming experience of realizing the meaning of it all – what the universe is all about, what we are here for, what time and space are all about – in fact, the meaning of the whole multi-dimensional consciousness and energy that we call the cosmos. This experience has been called 'omniscience', which means 'all-knowing', and the person who 'comes back' from it realizes at last that there is a profound meaning to everyone's life. The only problem is that the realization is so multi-dimensional and all-embracing that it is impossible to communicate it to other people. There is a quote that goes something like this: "That which is reality can't be spoken of, that which can be spoken of is not real."

POINTS TO REMEMBER

· We all have the entire chakra qualities active all the time, but in each of us some are stronger than others.
· During the day and over time, we move up and down in each group, but each of us has a fairly stable level ongoing in our life.
· The higher our stable level, the more constant is our ongoing stability.
· Drugs and other experiences can move us to a higher level for a time, and then we drop! That is the secret of addiction to anything.
· The process of yoga as it gradually evolves the qualities of the chakras is a stable development, and stays with us.

This completes our overview of the evolvement of the various aspects of the personality as seen from the perspective of the chakra systems. We can now look at the effects on our personality of the different chakra aspects that are dominant in each of us. As mentioned above, we all have the entire chakra qualities active all the time, but in each of us, some are stronger than others. What does this mean for our day to day activities, and for the progress of our evolution?

9

Different Chakra Aspects Dominant in each Individual

Even though each one of us has all of the chakra aspects active, we tend to 'specialize' in one or two of them, and the ones that are more active in us will contribute more strongly to our own personality style. Some people are very strong in one chakra aspect, so its particular style determines the whole course of their life and its direction. This is certainly one part of our personality that causes us to differ from each other. Yoga works to balance the activities of the six chakras so that we develop a balanced and more understanding personality.

Summary of strengths of expression of the different aspects of the personality

Here is a summary of the main characteristics of people with one chakra system dominant. What is described is around the 'ordinary' level – rajas – of evolvement of the particular chakra's qualities.

Mooladhara dominant: These people spend much of their life preoccupied with their security. They think a lot about their personal safety and that of their family, about collecting and keeping money and possessions, and they try to plan for the future to the ultimate degree.

Swadhisthana dominant: These people don't care much about security, power, compassion, intellect, etc.; they are much more interested in sexual exploits and other ways of having a good time. Of course, joy, humour and other swadhisthana qualities sweeten our lives, but the pleasure desires must be kept in their place – other aspects are important too.

Manipura dominant: These people don't even think much about security or having fun; they prefer to get things done and accumulate power so that they can accomplish those things. They are the 'power people'.

Anahata dominant: These people don't care much about any of those other things. They are preoccupied with caring and compassion, and they are very concerned with and hurt by evidence of non-caring, either about themselves or others.

Vishuddhi dominant: These people are much more interested in passing on information and keeping up communication.

Ajna dominant: These are the thinkers, who are uncomfortable if they are disturbed in their cogitations.

Obviously we all have these different expressions of our personality, but as each of us specializes in one or two, in addition to creating differences in us, they make us vulnerable to related situations in our lives, such as insecurity, sexuality, loss of control, etc. We then identify these situations as stressful. Remember that because of these sorts of differences, stress is a very personal thing. One person's stressful situation is another person's exhilaration, and in another that situation is just met with apathy.

THE MOOLADHARA DOMINANT CHARACTERS

Security

The people who have mooladhara chakra more activated are preoccupied with their personal safety and security, and that of other members of their family. They spend a lot of their time thinking of how to accumulate money or possessions. Their conversations are usually about material things, and their input such as reading, watching TV and going to lectures are about how to make and invest money, and accumulate property. There is good sense in this, of course, and people who are living in the world and have day-to-day responsibilities need to be responsible for the security in the present and to provide for the future. However, a person with a highly activated mooladhara is very much concerned with such things. It's not that they are particularly insecure (that is the experience of the person with the tamasic mooladhara), it is just that they are preoccupied with, and give a lot of their time and energy to, security and the material possessions they think will ensure it.

The misers

Danny de Vito, the American movie actor, was in a movie called *Other People's Money* a number of years ago, and the character he played gave his philosophy of life. He said, "Life's a game – it's a game in which you accumulate as much money as you can, and the one who has the most money when he dies wins the game." To him, the whole object of life is collecting and accumulating money. This is the attitude of the person who is stuck in mooladhara chakra. These are the people Freud called the anal-retentive personalities – they are even constipated – they can't let anything go. But of course the more they accumulate, the more worried they are about losing it, and that is their vulnerability, that is what causes them the most stress in life. Only recently a magazine in the United States did a survey of multi-millionaires, and almost all of them said that their worst worry was losing money.

Summary according to the gunas
Tamasic level
· Personal survival is the key to this person's life.
· Fear is the ruling emotion.
· Like the animal in the jungle, they may attack if threatened, but it is defensive, not like the power-based aggression of manipura.
· Paranoia is the extreme of this tamasic state.

- They can be obsessed with money and material security, but because of the tamas they are not good at getting them, so they can become desperate, and may resort to crime.
- At a higher level are the misers who come by their money and possessions legally, but can't let them go.

Rajasic level
- They think a lot about their security and that of their loved ones.
- Keen to collect and use the money and possessions they think will ensure security. Often they see money as just a medium to make more money.
- Conversation and past-times are about making money, the stock market, 'get rich quick schemes', real estate investments, etc. Often that's 'all' they talk about.
- They plan for the future to the ultimate degree and spend almost as much time in the future as they do counting their money.

Sattwic level
- Very interested in accumulating material things to do good work, and are good at it.
- Many of them have the 'Midas touch' but without Midas's problem. In India, people would say they are blessed by Lakshmi, the divine aspect of prosperity.
- Because they are basically secure within themselves, they don't become attached to material possessions, or suffer if they don't get them.
- So they are free to use them in the interests of the requirements of the other chakras, usually for service.

THE SWADHISTHANA DOMINANT CHARACTERS

Joy and sexuality

Many people have a joyous nature and a good sense of humour, and the sexual side of their life is fulfilling and appropriate. However, people with a highly activated swadhisthana chakra are preoccupied with sex, and spend most of their time thinking about it or trying to 'get' it. They relate to other people in a sexual way, even when the context has nothing to do with sex, such as in the workplace. They are the hedonists.

The hedonists

As the swadhisthana qualities are sex and other forms of enjoyment, the people whose attention is mainly centred there are preoccupied with enjoyment and plenty of sex. Their main object in life is to avoid as many problems as possible and just try to 'whoop it up' in pleasant excitement, and having fun all the time. It seems that nowadays a large proportion of our Western population have that point of view – that the object of life is to have a good time, get as many comforts as you can and eliminate as many difficulties as possible. Not for them the Danny de Vito hoarding of money; they say, "Spend it as soon as you get it", and the greater the thrill, the better. But these are the vulnerabilities that hold them down in the lower levels, in debt and addictions, and which cause them the most stress.

Summary according to the gunas
Tamasic level

· These are the people with chronic lifelong depression of varying degrees.
· Their life can be one of a tamasic hell on earth.
· They may be sufficiently activated by rajas to actively pursue pleasure, but it is a desperate quest, and they go to places of low tamasic vibration to get it. As a result the whole endeavour can end in trouble.
· If activated by some rajas, they may have sexual drives, but their sexual activities are just a desperate attempt to experience some joy which causes trouble anyway. Why?
  a) The sex depletes their already low energy.
  b) The sexuality is exploitative, so it causes complications with the partners, and possibly guilt.

Rajasic level

- Two words describe these people: sexy and hedonistic.
- Preoccupied with sex, they relate to people in a sexual way in inappropriate contexts.
- They pursue enjoyment and the avoidance of difficulties, often to the exclusion of life's duties.
- They consider money just useful for having fun.
- Their main vulnerabilities are debt, addictions and ill-advised sexual exploits.

Sattwic level

- People who have swadhisthana highly activated at this level spend their lives in a happy carefree state. At higher levels they can be quite blissful, but they are always mindful of the needs of others.
- Their joy is infectious, and they are popular wherever they go.
- If they have enough activity in the other aspects of personality to maintain their lives, they can have a very good existence indeed.

THE MANIPURA DOMINANT CHARACTERS

Power and dynamic action

The person with a well-balanced manipura has good self-esteem, ample energy for the work that has to be done, and the ability to encourage other people to help. But the people with a strongly active manipura are really preoccupied with personal power and controlling all aspects of their lives and other people's – the 'control freaks'. They are competitive in all situations, including ones that require not power but love and tenderness, such as intimate relationships. The power of their manipura floods over into all aspects of their life, and their marriages are usually battlegrounds instead of loving and mutually fulfilling partnerships. It is mainly in these areas that they are most vulnerable as loneliness descends on them later in their lives.

The power brokers

Alfred Adler, a disciple of Freud, studied the power types, and saw the association with self-esteem. It was he who coined the term 'inferiority complex' – in the lower areas of what we would call manipura chakra types. One famous American a few decades ago uttered the statement: "The greatest aphrodisiac is power." It's easy to see the 'favourite' chakra system of that person. But the power person's downfall, and their greatest stresses, also revolve around the loss or possible loss of power. Even if they are at the 'top of the heap', they are surrounded by other power people who are 'breathing down their necks' – not a very comfortable position.

Summary according to the gunas
Tamasic level
- At the lowest level these people are just unable to accomplish the simplest requirements necessary to run their lives.
- People with more rajas are dominated by the desire for power, but it is corrupted by the darkness of tamas, with its ignorance of other people's needs, and tendency to be harmful to others in the pursuit of what they want.
- If they are smart they become dictators, if they are not they are bullies, if they are charming, maybe even manipulative politicians.
- They form the pool of people from which violent criminals and standover men come.

Rajasic level
- These people love power and control in all areas of their life – 'control freaks'.
- Politicians, administrators, managers, military.
- They see power everywhere.
- They are competitive even where love and tenderness are needed, such as in intimate relationships. They must realize this or their marriages (all of them) will become battlegrounds.

Sattwic level

- Excellent managers of charitable and humanitarian institutions, etc.
- They love power for the work it can produce, not for ego, so they can be very productive.
- Their power is lubricated with love.
- They get the work done because people love to help them.
- Explain the selfless service of karma yoga (dealt with in Chapter 13) to them and they understand instantly.
- Non-egotistical work as an instrument of grace comes naturally to them.

THE ANAHATA DOMINANT CHARACTERS

Love and related emotions

People are generally able to experience and show their feelings at appropriate times, use their intellect at other appropriate times, and perform appropriate actions at other times. However, the person with a highly active anahata chakra emotionalizes most aspects of their life. This can be a pleasant thing if the quality of the emotion is positive, such as love and compassion, and the person has a suitable lifestyle outlet for them, such as the helping, nurturing or religious professions. But many can just as easily become embroiled in negative emotional states such as feelings of hurt, resentment, jealousy, hate, dejection, fear, etc., and their life becomes a hell. Bhakti yoga, the concentrated pursuit of devotion, prayer, compassion and service for the benefit of others, is recommended to develop such a person. They should also pursue the other branches of yoga to gain insight into their personalities.

The warm hearts

These people believe that feelings are the only important thing, that compassion is of prime importance, that the sole object of life is to actually go out and help other people. They are starting to get close to the truth, but if they are

132

too much governed by anahata chakra, without the balance of the other chakra qualities, they render themselves very vulnerable to hurt. They can also become so preoccupied with the tragedies of the world that they ignore the good things and their lives become filled with misery about the terrible things that are happening. They can be so frustrated about not being able to do anything that they have difficulty getting out of the negative morass. Not only that, but they are easily misunderstood by other people who can't see what all the fuss is about.

Summary according to the gunas
Tamasic level
- To call these people 'anahata active' is a misnomer because tamas is the curse of inactivity, and the curse of non-love. The people who have their predominant chakra activity at anahata at the dark tamasic level can be uncaring of others and possibly dangerous because of it. In addition, if they are more activated by rajas, they have another problem. Anahata is the main centre of emotions, but because of the 'darkness' of tamas their emotions are mainly negative, with little of the positive. Their refuge is bhakti yoga to transmute their negative emotions into devotion.

Rajasic level
- For these people compassion is the driving force in their lives, and they may do a lot of good, but they may also run into the problem of negative emotions such as emotional pain at the plight of others, resentment and anger about the injustices of the world. They need to remember to stay positive and concentrate on the good work done in the spirit of karma yoga and bhakti yoga.

Sattwic level
- A lifetime of compassion and care for the welfare of others is the hallmark of these people. Most of them work in a small way, unnoticed but not concerned about that. Some

of them, such as Gandhi, accomplish great things; they are the obvious benefactors of the world. Their viewpoint of life is observing the needs of others and addressing any injustices. They may be spiritually devotional as well as socially benevolent, such as Gandhi and Mother Theresa.

THE VISHUDDHI DOMINANT CHARACTERS

Communication

We can see around us people with all ranges of vishuddhi chakra activation. Some hardly say anything; if they are in a group, they are happy to just listen. Some are so isolated that they don't even take part in any groups. Other people can state their point and then listen to what others have to say. Others can't stop talking; their drive to communicate their information keeps it pouring out, irrespective of what else is going on around them. If there is nobody there to talk to, they will pick up the phone and find someone, or they will go out looking for someone, and if none of that works, they will write a letter or an e-mail. These are the people with very active vishuddhi systems – the compulsive communicators.

Compulsive communicators (bores)

To these people, who have the vishuddhi system dominant and are under the influence of rajas, the most important thing in life is to have plenty of others around them with whom to communicate. They may accept the two-way flow of opinions, but especially they like to give their opinions. They are always willing to give their opinion, whether they know anything about the subject or not. They just talk past all the 'ifs' and 'buts', and they end all their statements (to take a breath) in a grammatical conjunction such as 'and', 'but', 'however', etc., so the other person has no entry point for a comment. If the other person yawns a lot, the vishuddhi people are usually too busy talking to notice, but if they do, they only assume that the person is tired.

Needless to say, the most stressful condition for them is to have nobody around to talk to. That happens a lot because they bore other people, who then avoid them, and a typical vicious circle occurs. These people become lonely easily, and it is very painful for them. As their vishuddhi system becomes more evolved, they develop more considerate and subtle ways of communicating. They can become quite powerful communicators for good, and can also become quite telepathic. With the help of yoga, their other chakra qualities become more robust, and their relationships with other people become more balanced.

Summary according to the gunas

Tamasic level

- At this level the communication of vishuddhi is usually stuck down in the inertia of tamas; very little communication.
- However, if the person has some rajas influencing their communication, it will usually be corrupted. At the least they will be complainers who spread the negativity of tamas for all to hear, or tricky fast-talking salesmen. At worst they will be poison-tongued troublemakers who spread malicious rumours and try to destroy the reputations of others.

Rajasic level

- These are the people who are most contented if they make their life one of teaching, speaking or entertainment. They enjoy having an audience, and if their self-esteem is good, they feel happy in front of audiences of thousands.
- At the social level they may be the 'life of the party', but at a more negative level such a person may be the talkative bore who chatters on and ignores the opinions (or even the yawns) of other people.

Sattwic level

- The people who are specialized at the sattwic levels of vishuddhi are those with the power to sway large numbers of people with the higher truths. At this level they are really the instruments for the eloquent communication of grace.

· St Francis said, "Lord, make me an instrument of thy peace." Like St Francis, these people spend their life being such an instrument through the medium of communication

THE AJNA DOMINANT CHARACTERS

Intellect, intuition, wisdom, psychic abilities etc.

These are the qualities of ajna chakra, and they are positive and helpful if used appropriately. The yogis are keen to develop ajna chakra, and many of the yoga practices are for that purpose, but they emphasize that it should be developed and evolved in a balanced way with all the other chakra qualities, not in isolation.

The intellectuals

These people are the logical thinkers, which is a popular way to be in the scientific West. They tend to deal with each situation in a logical, non-emotional way, even if it really requires action or the expression of feelings. From the point of view of stress, they are fairly insulated because they are not overly worried about security, seeking pleasure, power, love or companionship. But they can be stressed by not having enough information from which to reach logical conclusions. As their ajna chakra develops, though, they develop bursts of intuition to fill the gaps in the available information. They are also stressed by anybody disturbing their reading or their reverie – their 'mantra' in life is: "Don't disturb me, I'm reading"

Summary according to the gunas

Tamasic level

· The qualities of ajna chakra do not lend themselves to being fully tamasic. However, people whose lifetime of thinking is tainted by tamas can be just poor quality thinkers. If the content of their thinking is corrupted, they may spend their whole life devising tricky ways to satisfy the lower urges of the other chakras, such as cheating people out of their money, lying for sexual pleasures, for gaining power, etc.

Rajasic level

- The person with ajna dominant at the rajasic level is often too busy *thinking* to actually *do* anything. They may esteem the intellect so much that they have disregard or even contempt for intuition, feelings, constructive activities or spiritual faith. Their belief in the primacy of the intellect is generally supported in Western society, so they are usually comfortably immune to any viewpoints apart from the logic of the rational mind.

Sattwic level

- These people spend their lives in the pursuit of truth, and as they are coming into tune with the information and processes of the higher mind, they are finding the answers.
- At the highest levels they are in contact with elevated levels of mind, where they have access to intuition and wisdom. The conclusions they reach under such influences are true, and their behaviour based on them is faultless.
- They also have access to higher powers.

KEEP IT BALANCED

Remember:
- One of the main functions of many yoga practices is to act directly on our chakras, and evolve our different personality qualities that way.
- But the key to the yoga path, in all its dimensions, is always BALANCE.

As an example of the need to keep balance, people often ask to be given yoga practices to develop their ajna chakra because they would like to be able to read people's minds or see their auras. They think again when asked how they would feel if they *did know* what other people were thinking, and realized that the people didn't like them. Wouldn't they need to have plenty of the security of mooladhara chakra so they wouldn't feel threatened, and the humour of swadhisthana chakra so that they could laugh at it, and the self-esteem of manipura chakra so they wouldn't feel embarrassed? Wouldn't they need the love of anahata chakra so they could love the person anyway, and the free communication of vishuddhi so they could continue to relate to the person, and the intuition of ajna to tell them why so that they could do something about it, or about themselves? They usually then decide to 'go with the yogis' and keep it all balanced.

This is one of the main principles of the practice of yoga, to energize all the chakras in a balanced way. If we are giving a class of postures, for instance, a good teacher will give at least one asana for each chakra, or a combination technique such as Salute to the Sun (Surya Namaskara) which works on all of them. If an ordinary yoga teacher is giving mantras, they should give general mantras that work on all the chakras. If we are giving concentration practices, they should be holistic, such as the rotation of awareness on the body parts in Yoga Nidra, or the rotation of consciousness in the whole spine, or concentration on all of the chakras. Even when we are practising karma yoga, the world around us usually supplies a rich variety of experiences so that each of the chakra qualities comes into play as the day goes on. This key principle of yoga – BALANCE, certainly applies to the qualities of the chakras.

NO WONDER WE CAN'T
UNDERSTAND EACH OTHER

Imagine if you gave your money to charity, or to some good cause, or to someone who was 'down and out', the Danny de Vito character would consider that absolutely ridiculous, and would be sure you were an idiot. He would even suspect your motives; he would be sure there was some gain in it for you because to him it would be absolutely inconceivable to give away money without getting more in return, wouldn't it? "What's in it for you?"

What would the hedonist think of you if you underwent hardships for other people as did Dr Albert Schweitzer, or Dr Fred Hollowes, the Australian eye surgeon who lived in Eritrea working for no payment, under difficult conditions, doing cataract operations to cure blind people there, or Mother Theresa and her nuns in Kolkata? Now the Danny de Vito character *and* the hedonists would think that was absolutely ridiculous. "No payment? Rotten living conditions? Must be crazy!" Someone who was 'specializing' in the pleasures of swadhisthana chakra, running after enjoyment, would certainly wonder why you were there putting up with all those hardships instead of having a good time. But the anahata chakra person knows; they will even give up a position of power to a person they believe will do the job better if it will benefit people in need. To the manipura person that is plain insanity!

This is one of the main problems with our relationships with each other; we have different motivations in life, partly because we specialize in different chakra qualities. We then imagine that is how everybody is, and are baffled when they don't behave the 'right' way. Yoga helps us to relate to other people by making us become aware of ourselves and these differences from other people so that we can understand where other people are 'coming from'. It balances the expressions of those qualities within us so we are able to empathize with others. And it helps us to evolve the qualities of our own chakra systems so that we can understand other people's perceptions of their lives, their thinking patterns, their emotions and their behaviour – after all, we have been there ourselves, so we know.

BUT THEY DON'T KNOW!

It is important to remember that people who are especially active in one chakra aspect don't realize it. To them that is just the way to be; in fact, it is the way *everyone* should be.

To the mooladhara dominated person, the world simply consists of 'haves' and 'have-nots', and they see the whole of life as a competition for a limited supply of resources to ensure a secure future. If they are highly active at a low level of expression of the mooladhara quality, they will be acquisitive even to the point of crime if they really feel insecure or want something enough. No amount of reasoning will convince them that *generosity can be a better plan for their future* than greed; that just doesn't make sense to them.

To the swadhisthana person, life and the world is simply a source of pleasures that have to be pursued (called *raga* in yoga) and painful experiences that have to be avoided (called *dwesha* in yoga). They are often prepared to use all their resources to that end, and are always in danger of addiction to drugs, people, gambling, etc. But they just accept all the suffering they experience as part of life. To them the 'pleasure principle', as Freud called it, is all there is in life, and any suggestion that we can outgrow desires and aversions falls on deaf ears.

To the manipura person, life is nothing more than a competition between people for the power to do what they want to. If we remonstrate with them to be more democratic, to get some consensus, to share the decisions, they don't even know what we are talking about.

To the person strong in anahata, life is a collection of victims and rescuers, usually with themselves as the willing rescuer – but often turning out to be the victim. They can be very emotional people, sometimes with positive and negative emotions alternating at a dizzying pace, and it can be most painful for them. But they are incapable of understanding other people who are not living according to their feelings. They consider that any advice to the contrary is a demonstration of just how heartless and non-caring other people are.

To the person with an overactive vishuddhi chakra "all the world's a stage, and all the men and women merely players", as Shakespeare wrote. And every one of those players should be a willing ear for such a person. It is inconceivable to them that people are not interested in their latest endeavour or adventure. It is not possible to explain the situation to them; it just causes them to feel misunderstood for a while, and then they are off onto another subject.

The person who is specializing in ajna chakra is often too busy *thinking* to actually *do* anything. They may think up grandiose plans that never come to anything, but it doesn't matter because by then they are thinking up something else. Everything in their life must obey the laws of logic. So must the people around them, and here's the problem; everybody is not logical, many are guided by their feelings, some may even use intuition. This is not acceptable to our ajna people, who consider them all 'idiots' – a word they often use. If we try to explain this to them, we are just not being logical, so we are idiots too.

What is the solution to all this? Yoga helps in a number of ways, for instance:

1. By evolving the qualities of the dominant chakra, the person is able to function at a higher level of quality than the attitudes and behaviours mentioned above. Then the aptitudes and skills of that dominant chakra can really make the person a power for good.
2. Yoga brings up the activities of the other chakra systems towards a balance.
3. Practitioners of yoga develop more awareness of the characteristics and needs of others, so the qualities of their dominant chakra system don't impact negatively.
4. Insight into our own behaviour allows us to realize that we do in fact have an overactive chakra system.
5. It also allows us to modify the effects from that dominant chakra system.

BUT THE CHAKRA ACTIVITIES VARY TOO

As we have discussed, according to the make-up of our constitution, we will each have a reasonably stable pattern of more activation of some chakras. But within that fairly steady state, some variations occur from hour to hour, day to day, month to month, etc. due to internal and external influences in our lives. Maybe weather, the earth's magnetic fields and even cosmic events can activate some chakra circuits and not others. For instance, my observations have led me to believe that a particular phase of the moon will 'light up' the same chakra in all of us during that phase, often causing those people who have a lot of activity already in a particular chakra to experience effects in the physical, energy, emotional, mental and possibly psychic aspects of that chakra. This is suggested in the following group of observations.

Have you noticed this?
Back in the early 1970s, when I was working as a family medical practitioner, I noticed something mysterious. A lot of my practice was spinal adjustments, using techniques I had learnt from two other doctors who were experts in the field. It dawned on me one morning that almost all the people in that session had come with lower neck and arm problems. Days later, the 'new' people who came were nearly all there for lumbago and sciatica, and there were no new neck problems.

As the weeks went by I realized that this was no coincidence, and that there was a rhythm to it. First the people with the upper neck problems would come in, then a couple of days later a different group of people with problems of the lower neck and arms, then thoracic spine and chest, then upper lumbar, then lower lumbar and legs. Then it would go back up the other way. What was the cause of this pattern? I thought of all sorts of things from the weather to the television news, then it dawned on me – the rhythm could be the phases of the moon.

142

Prior to that, I had known about the influence of the moon when I lived and worked in psychiatric hospitals as I trained to be a psychiatrist. The nursing staff were convinced that the patients with agitated conditions, such as acute schizophrenia, mania and agitated depressions, were more disturbed at the time of the full moon. As time went on it became obvious to me that it was true in our hospital. In fact, later when I was Deputy Superintendent of another hospital and responsible for the after-hours roster of the medical staff, I always rostered myself to work on nights of the new moon. I slept undisturbed. Needless to say I would not be as devious as that nowadays.

The appearance of spinal problems at different levels was something new though. The upper cervical problems with their migraine headaches came at the time of the full moon, then as the moon waned, in came the lower cervical and arm troubles, then thoracic, then upper lumbar, then the lower lumbar and sciatica at new moon. Then as the moon waxed, it occurred the other way. Not only that, as I was also conducting a normal family practice, I began to notice a predominance of people with all sorts of head problems coming in anew at the time of the full moon. Then as the moon waned, the chronic arm and lower neck problems would flare up, then the chests, then the abdominal problems such as peptic ulcers and irritable bowel, etc., then the urinary tract and lower bowel, then the legs and feet at new moon.

Sometimes it was a new condition, sometimes it was an ongoing chronic one 'flaring up', but in most cases its location was in time with its phase of the moon. I thought it was rather funny that I was getting the credit (and payment) for relieving those people of their symptoms within a few days, when the moon should have received at least most of the credit. It also suggested something else too: maybe many people who are having on-going treatment for some chronic disorder only need it at their 'flare-up' phase of the moon cycle. It may be something to think about in the healing professions.

In later years, as I travelled around the world as a sannyasin, teaching yoga and learning all sorts of things, I noticed other effects from the moon phases. For example, people out and about on the two days leading up to and during the full moon were, in general, more impulsive and agitated. I realized it first when I was driving a car all around the United States in the early 1980s, both in other people and myself. We were more impatient, would push into small spaces in traffic, pedestrians would hurry dangerously in front of the car; everybody seemed in a hurry. Then like a miracle, as soon as the moon started to wane, we all settled down. I still see it now.

However, some people experienced the opposite effect. At one time, in a place where I stayed in South America, the cook was a woman who had been born in early July. Every month (not related to her menstruation), at the new moon, she was depressed, surly and withdrawn; she used to hide in a cupboard, and we had to coax her out to cook the dinner, which usually turned out to taste mediocre at best. Then as the moon waxed every month, so did she. She started to exude vitality, she became friendly and loving, and the food became better and better. Then at the full moon she absolutely glowed and the food was cordon bleu.

It occurred in the yoga classes too. The student's joints being activated at the level of the moon phase would stiffen up, and have to be given extra gentle stretching to avoid strain. It was obvious especially in the flexibility practices (*Pawanmuktasana 1*), in which all the joints of the body are stretched in turn. In the major asanas, people would say, "It's funny, I could do this asana easily during the week, now I can't get into the position." It was usually an asana for the chakra area that was being 'lit up' at its phase of the moon.

Maybe in meditation, and in daily life, the mental material we are working on is partly that of the chakra activated by its phase of the moon. Such as intellect and intuition at full moon, communication as the moon starts to wane, love, hate and hurt as anahata becomes more active, power and self-esteem at middle moon, sexuality and emotions surrounding joy and sadness when it is swadhisthana's turn, and security at the time of the new moon. My observations lead me to believe it is true. What about yours?

Of course, the events around us will help to determine our mind-set, but maybe they are also influenced by the moon's phases because the people around us are similarly influenced, and it is they who trigger most of our joys and sorrows. Moreover, no matter what is impinging on us, maybe we react to it differently according to the phase of the moon and which of our 'buttons can be pressed' most easily at that time.

Swami Satyananda has said that we are all slowly evolving anyway, yoga hurries it up. In yoga we practise techniques to activate and awaken the chakra systems, so that we empty ourselves of the personality blockages associated with them. Maybe the moon, as it passes through its phases, helps us in this, as one of the instruments that is driving our natural evolution, by activating the chakras and forcing us to confront the pleasures and pains of our expanding personalities.

Self-knowledge

Irrespective of what causes the temporary variations in the activity of our chakra systems, we certainly each have some chakras that are our 'favourites'. This effect is an important variable in the formation of our personality, and a factor to be reckoned with as we work to evolve ourselves.

Let us go on now, and put together all the different elements we have been discussing, and see how they combine with each other to form a multi-dimensional model of the human personality. Remember though, this is not just a model, it is a functional grouping of established yogic entities, and the whole thing is amenable to development and evolvement by established classical yogic practices.

10

A Seven-Dimensional Model of the Personality

When we dealt with the expressions of the different aspects of the chakras, we looked at each according to the different elements of human expression thus:

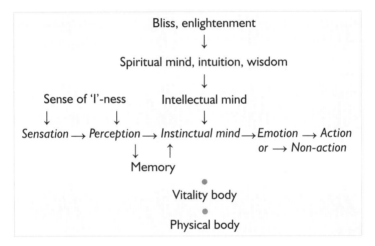

Points to note so far

1. For each chakra system we have dealt with how each of the above elements expresses itself through the aspects of that chakra. However, let us look at that diagram again – it could also give us an instant picture of the expressions of any chakra system at any point of time, and this would include how evolved it is. For instance, there would be a big

difference between how a person expressing a tamasic level of a chakra right at this moment and one expressing a sattwic level of the same chakra would be perceiving their world, thinking, feeling, behaving, etc.

2. There would be 48 ways of expressing the levels of evolvement of the qualities of the six chakra systems, even if we take just the eight sub-divisions of the gunas we have used here, i.e.: Tamasic, Tamasic-Rajasic, Rajasic-Tamasic, Rajasic, Rajasic-Sattwic, Sattwic-Rajasic, Sattwic and Enlightened.

3. Also remember that each chakra system in its state of evolution at any time will express itself through the ten ways of expression we have dealt with i.e.: Physical, Vitality, 'I'-ness, Perception, Memory, Instinctual mind, Intellectual mind, Higher mind, Emotions and feelings, and Actions.

4. So this gives us a large number of ways (480) in which the aspects of the chakra systems in a person can express themselves at any point of time. This all then contributes to a multi-dimensional model of human personality.

Let us look at personality again. The definition we gave at the beginning was: "The distinctive and characteristic patterns of *perception, memory, thought, emotions and behaviour* that define an individual's *personal style* of interacting with the physical and social environments." That is adequate for most purposes, but according to yoga there are more valid purposes, and so to complete the picture we really need to include all the ten ways in which we are expressing ourselves at any time.

The ten modes of expression

How these expressions will be depends on the chakra system that is active at the time and the level of evolution of its qualities.

Physical: Body posture, facial expression, how am I standing, how am I sitting, how am I walking, how am I talking, any tensions, any restlessness or agitation, unique subtle body language, other subliminal body communications, etc.

Vitality: General vitality and subtle manifestations such as charisma and 'magnetism' (how much we attract others).

'I'-ness: One's obvious sense of self-esteem, and degree of ego. What is the degree of my sense of oneness with, or separation from others?

Perception: My personal and unique way of 'taking in' my world – what am I, at this moment, selecting from the vast panorama (and what am I ignoring or denying)?

Memory: Obviously we all have very different contents in our memory stores. Some are pleasant, some are traumatic – how much of each? How tightly are they repressed? Which are active at this time?

Instinctual mind: The habitual thinking styles that are unique to each of us and our personal regular thought content – how am I thinking and what am I thinking at this moment?

Intellectual mind: How well can I use it? Is it logical? Does it make sense? Is distorted thinking causing me distress?

Higher mind: Am I able to access it at all, if so how much? Is it available at this moment or am I caught down in the lower 'dramas'?

Emotions and feelings: The quality of these – hate or love, guilt or joy, anger or gentleness, etc. What emotions or feelings am I experiencing at present?

Actions: The quality of these – kind or cruel, fine or coarse, generous or exploitative, etc. How am I behaving now?

What determines how we are expressing these at any point in time?

· The aspects inherent in our chakra systems active at that time.
· Evolution of our chakra systems.
· Balance or imbalance of the activities of our chakra systems.
· Our balance of ida/pingala.
· Which of the above avenues of expression are dominant at that time.

The aspects inherent in our chakra systems

What determines the 'subject' of the particular life question with which I am preoccupied at any moment? The particular chakra aspect that is active.

If my anahata chakra system is 'switched on' at the moment, I may well be involved with love and affection. If so, my *body* will be in the posture of loving, caring, supporting, etc. My *energies* will be directed to the loved one. My sense of *'I'-ness*, my identity, will be that of a person who is loving and experiencing a oneness instead of separation. I will be *perceiving* my world as a loving place. The *memories* coming into my awareness will probably be about previous loving experiences. I will be *thinking* loving thoughts of a quality appropriate to the level of mind at which I am identified *(instinctual, intellectual or higher)*. My *feelings* will be of love, caring, intimacy, and my *actions* will be of caressing, comforting, helping, etc.

However, in this anahata case, my expressions could be otherwise – maybe negative ones. That depends on other factors which we will also discuss, but they will also express themselves through the ten categories, and the 'subject' will still be about the aspects of the anahata system – love and compassion.

For any of the chakra systems, its activation will virtually 'choose the subject' with which I will be preoccupied at any time. The *subject of my attention* will be the *aspect* of that particular *chakra system*.

Evolution of the aspects of our chakra systems

So when one is occupied within the subject of one of the chakra systems, what determines the *quality* of one's expressions of the aspects of that system? The answer of course is the *evolution of those aspects*.

This brings us to the third level of this practical yogic model of personality (after the koshas and the chakra qualities). This is where the level of evolution makes itself felt. We have chosen to make examples of just eight guna levels of evolution, but there are really no distinct dividing lines between them, so the increments are infinite. However, for the sake of simplicity, let's stick to the eight:

· Tamasic
· Tamasic-Rajasic
· Rajasic-Tamasic
· Rajasic
· Rajasic-Sattwic
· Sattwic-Rajasic
· Sattwic
· Enlightened.

Now each of the ten expressions of the aspects of the chakra system active at this moment will reflect the degree of evolution of those aspects. If, as in the above example, anahata is active, the quality of the ten expressions (body, energy, 'I'-ness, perception, etc.) of the aspects of *love, compassion,* etc., will depend on the quality of evolution of those aspects. If they are sattwic, one's whole demeanour will be dramatically different from what it would be if they were tamasic or rajasic or anything in between.

Balance or imbalance of the activities of our chakra systems

Yes, but what determines which chakra system will be 'switched on' at this moment? Present circumstances may activate the appropriate chakra system. For instance, if my lovely wife walks up and gives me a hug, anahata will come on loud and clear – maybe even swadhisthana (joy). If, on the other hand, someone walks up and puts a wad of $100 notes into my hand, mooladhara is likely to start buzzing, but the anahata system may get some exercise too.

Another way that a chakra system can be activated is to just *think* about the qualities of that system. Possibly the best known are angry thoughts activating the adrenaline system, or sexual fantasizing switching on that whole process, and there's not even anybody in sight.

These are appropriate responses to the stimuli, but sometimes one or two of our chakra systems are so active that they drown out the others. They dominate our thinking, emotions, behaviour and all our other expressions. This constitutes the fourth dimension of our personality model – the chakra system that is customarily dominant.

Even though each one of us has all the chakra aspects active, we tend to 'specialize' in one or two of them, and the ones that are more active in us contribute more strongly to our own personality style. How can I tell which aspects are most active in me? Simple! What am I most interested in? What do I think of most of the time? What really 'turns me on'? Which of all those qualities of the chakra systems we have been discussing do I most identify with? Got your answer?

One of the greatest problems with 'specializing' in a chakra or two is that they might overshadow the more appropriate responses of the other chakra systems. For instance, if the person caught up in the thinking of ajna chakra is contemplating the theory of relativity when he is making love, it won't work. Or conversely if the boss is thinking of sex while giving dictation to a secretary (yes, it happens), the quality of the letters will be poor.

'Balance' is one of the key concepts of the whole system of yoga, and virtually all of the practices aim to accomplish this. Balancing the activities of all the chakra systems is what we may call our 'vertical balance'. What about our 'horizontal balance'?

Our balance of ida/pingala

The fifth dimension of our model of human personality is whether we are expressing ourselves through the style of the left brain (pingala), the right brain (ida) or the balance between the two (sushumna).

Up to this point we have discussed the way we are functioning through all ten forms of expression as already modified by:
1. The aspects of the chakra system that is currently active
2. The degree of evolution of those qualities.

But another influence on this expression is whether we are in the pingala mode with its extroversion and other characteristics, the ida mode with its introversion, etc., or the balance between the two – the sushumna mode. As we have discussed, this will depend especially on the flow of the air through the nostrils. With yoga practices we can vary this as we choose, as long as the nostrils are structurally normal. So we can decide which of these three modes are influencing our expressions.

Which of the ten avenues of expression are dominant?

Now we come to the sixth variant (the seventh being the flow of the ten expressions themselves), which overlies all of the above. Which of the ten expressions is/are *dominant in an ongoing way* in each of us? We tend to 'specialize' in one or two of these; for instance, the thinkers who stay pretty much in their thoughts, the feelers who have strong emotional reactions about most things, the action types who get in and do things, often before properly thinking and feeling about them, the daydreamers who are much happier in their inner realms than dealing with the dramas of 'out here', and the observers who tend to see bigger pictures from 'above' the whole thing, and remain in the non-attached witness position. The other components of the 'ten' will have their adherents too. Remember that even though some people specialize in more than one, usually even they have a 'favourite'.

According to our model of personality, the favourite/s of the ten modes of expression will be the final factor that determines the ways in which we usually respond to our world around us, as it influences our personal style of interacting with the physical and social environments.

The seven dimensions of personality in a nutshell

1. *The koshas*: The different sheaths of the person – physical body, energy body, mind body, wisdom body and bliss body – give us an overall perspective of the human individual, the vast potential of each of us, and our similarities that we share right up to the highest level of consciousness.

However, it can explain differences between us also because most of us have a preponderance of our awareness concentrated in one of the five sheaths.

2. *The aspects of the chakra systems*: The chakra systems and their basic aspects such as security, joy, power, love, communication, intellect, intuition, etc., form the foundation stones of our personalities. One or other of them will be active at any time.

3. *Evolvement of the aspects*: The evolvement of the aspects of the individual chakra systems in a person as per the koshas is the key to our personal state of wellbeing, as well as the quality of our interactions in our world.

4. *Activation of the chakra systems*: The usual degree of activation of one or other of the different chakra systems in a person accentuates one group of aspects or another, and constitutes another variable on top of their evolvement. We strive for balance in this 'vertical direction'.

5. *Balance of ida and pingala*: From the perspective of *swara yoga* we assess whether we are expressing ourselves at any moment of time in a more introverted – *ida* – state, or a more extroverted – *pingala* – state. This is a personality variable over and above the evolution and activation. We strive for balance in this 'horizontal direction'.

6. *Our dominant expressions*: Which of the ten expressions are dominant in us? Are we thinkers, feelers, action types, daydreamers, observers, or balanced, high levels of mind? This adds another layer of variability to our personality style.

7. *Ultimate expression*: How we express ourselves in the ten ways mentioned above, through each of the aspects of the chakra systems themselves, ultimately determines our personal style of interacting with the physical and social environments.

How would we describe this?

How could we put this if we were describing a person's state at present? Remember this is what that person is doing now.

How about this: "A person under the influence of the . . . guna) quality of the . . . (chakra) aspects will be expressing themselves in the following way/s . . . (ten expressions)."

Or: "This person is . . . (expression/s) this way because they are presently under the influence of the . . . (guna) quality of the . . . (chakra) aspects."

The guna quality of the 'now' might be the usual guna quality of that chakra aspect in that person, or they may be just 'visiting' it – momentarily or for a certain period of their life.

Why that particular chakra aspect? It may be their favourite chakra, so they express it a lot, or it may have been activated at this time – momentarily or for a period of time (today, this week, this month, etc.).

How is the person expressing their state? Maybe with all of the ten modes (though the higher modes based on vijnanamaya and anandamaya koshas are not available to tamas and lower rajas). Alternatively, it may be only through one (or two) of them because, either it is their favourite expression, or that is what is required at this time.

Self-evolvement

So this seven-dimensional model of personality is not just a list, it is a unity. It describes seven interrelated yogic dimensions of the personality – each subsequent one being a set of dimensions additional to the preceding groups. The evolvement process acts on these, and constitutes an awareness of them, a balancing process and a refining/ purification. Next we will discuss the yoga practices that we use for this evolvement process, so we can understand how this all happens.

The Benefits of a Yogic Lifestyle

11

General Lifestyle Considerations

These next sections are not about 'no', they are about 'know'. This is not a sermon about our lifestyle sins. The object is simply to inform people about different aspects of their lifestyle that they may not know about. When I was in medical practice, both as a general practitioner and later as a psychiatrist, my patients would often come to me and say, "I'm not sleeping well, Doc. Would you please prescribe some sleeping pills?" My first question to them was, "What time in the day do you have your last cup of coffee or tea?" It is amazing how many had a cup of strong coffee just before bedtime; they didn't know that coffee contains caffeine which is a stimulant of the nervous system, and either keeps them awake or at least disturbs their sleep. So the first problem is that people often don't know what is best for their lifestyle. There is another problem too.

It's not easy to change our lifestyle
After more than 40 years of medical practice (and in my own personal life), it was obvious that people generally resist changing their lifestyle. People with high blood pressure found it easier to remain overweight, inactive, stressed and eating large amounts of salt than to rectify these before trying medication. Others, highly stressed by a destructive relationship, continued with it because it seemed easier than

becoming free from it. How often I have heard, "Don't worry about that stuff, Doc, just give me a pill."

Our present lifestyles are the culmination of decades of imitation of others, desire fulfilment, habit and expediency, among other things. Often our whole living and working spaces are moulded to accommodate our lifestyle, and in turn they help to perpetuate it – often an unhelpful vicious circle. Moreover, the people around us – our nearest and dearest – may also have a stake in maintaining their own status quo by keeping us in the situation, and use all sorts of subtle (and not so subtle) pressures to do so. Some people think there is no other way to live anyway, and they are surprised when they stay for a while in a yoga ashram or even another country and experience the benefits of another lifestyle altogether.

It is not easy to change, but often just minor improvements in a destructive lifestyle can have great benefits. So let us consider some of these, and assess some of their possible benefits. We will consider them under the following headings:

- General lifestyle
- Physical intake – what goes into the body
- Physical output – what comes out of the body
- Mental and emotional intake – negative intake, positive intake.

GENERAL LIFESTYLE

Simplicity

Some people have a very hectic life, and they often don't even realize it. They overwork, take their work home with them and do it late at night, and indulge in activities that cause them various kinds of anxieties and worries. A number of tendencies complicate people's lives. One is the inability to say no to people, so they accept more than they can handle, and end up handling none of it properly. Another potent source of complication is debt. One bad habit in Australia is for people to buy expensive (and really un-needed) gifts for the whole family as Christmas presents, and pay for it on their credit cards. Then they have a large amount of increasing debt to pay off for the rest of the year.

If we are stressed and seem to be running around in circles, it is a good idea to ask ourselves if our life has become too complicated. Then to write down all the things we do during the day, and those that seem to be causing our stress. Have I taken on too much? What can I cross off the list as unnecessary? Are there people in my life who are complicating it? Do they have to be there? How can I avoid expensive debt in future? (Remember the interest rate on credit cards is very high.) If I don't have enough money to pay off the credit card each month when it is due, can I really afford the card?

Regularity

Regular sleep is important. We should try to go to sleep at the same time every night, have our 6–8 hours as needed, then wake up early in the morning, ready to get going. The body clock (circadian rhythm) is quite regular, and although we won't have a nervous breakdown if we get it out of sync at times, regularity is best for our whole constitution. This makes it difficult for people on revolving shift work, whose scheduled period of work changes its starting time regularly, because their biological clock is always out of phase. Research has shown that it increases their stress levels as well as job inefficiency – the nuclear power plant disasters at Three Mile Island and Chernobyl were at least partially caused by this problem. There must be a solution to that problem apart from changing the job, but maybe that is the better option for some people.

Regular meals and regular yoga practices are also conducive to a lifestyle that keeps us in a stable and balanced condition, and help in our endeavours to evolve our personality.

159

Moderation

This is really about not overdoing it with any behaviours, especially those that can be addictive. Clearly, moderation in eating, sleeping, work, relationships, yoga practices, etc., helps us to avoid the extremes that throw body and mind out of balance.

Discipline

This is especially about the ability to set goals and move towards them. This allows us to flow with life without being swept away by it. Some people who have the problem of lack of discipline would find it helpful to organize their day, week, month or even year as a list on paper or in an electronic device. They should then try to stick to it – allowing of course for the inevitable unavoidable changes.

Efficiency

This includes such skills as organization, neatness, order, tidiness, economy of effort and materials, and time management. They seem to come naturally to many people, but only with great difficulty to others. When they are functioning properly, they can lubricate the progress of one's life very nicely. Many of them can be learnt as a formal study, and certainly yoga will help in their development.

PHYSICAL INTAKE
WHAT GOES INTO THE BODY

Back in more ancient times in India, the restrictions on what people took into their bodies were quite simple and pure common sense. They tended to avoid, for instance, eating meat partly because they observed the law of non-harming, but also because without a cooling system such as refrigeration, they could not stop it from deteriorating and becoming contaminated. Anyway, it didn't make sense to kill an ox that could be used to plough the rice paddy, or a cow that produced milk, more oxen and cows, and cleaned up the area by eating all the scraps around the place. It is no wonder cows are respected in India; they are so productive. The Indians and other groups such as Jews and Muslims especially didn't eat pork, probably because the pigs had a parasitic worm in their muscles that causes trichinosis, a very debilitating condition affecting many parts of the body.

Nowadays the food situation is more complicated. The old problems persist in some parts of the world, but in more modern parts, a whole crop of new ones have developed that would not have been dreamt of back in those times. Remember though, when trying to avoid taking in the substances I am going to mention, not to be a fanatic about it. Usually the body can easily cope with small amounts of impurities, so don't worry unduly if you have a small amount, which is often unavoidable, especially when we are not at home. Generally, it's what we take in on a regular basis that makes the difference. So let us consider some recommendations for our physical intake.

Pure food and water

Food and water that are free from contamination are taken for granted in the West, but it should be remembered that many people in the world are not so fortunate. The food and fluids they consume are contaminated with bacteria, parasites and chemical residues, which cause many of them to be seriously debilitated so that they can't even begin to develop themselves to a higher level. This is a major public health problem, which is being tackled worldwide by international bodies. Locally, such charities as our own Sivananda Math in India uses money donated to drill water bores and install hand pumps in the villages, so that people have pure water and don't have to drink out of contaminated wells.

Trans-fatty acids

Some forms of food processing, such as cooking in the microwave oven, and making margarine, change the fatty acids so that they may not be properly used by the cells. They are taken up to form the fats in the cell membranes, and presumably could cause the membranes to malfunction. This is very worrying because microwave cooking and eating margarine is now common worldwide. The immune cells in the blood are reproducing all the time at a great rate, so they would be expected to take up the greatest amount of the trans-fatty acids available.

Fats

Fats have become a major part of the Western diet, and they are of two types. The animal fats, which are found in meat and dairy products, have been amply demonstrated to cause disease of the arteries and cancer. The vegetable fats from seeds, nuts and some vegetable sources such as olives, avocado, etc., tend to protect against those conditions, but if eaten in large amounts, they just as easily cause obesity, with its own disease complications such as diabetes and high blood pressure.

It is interesting to note that in the last 30 years in the affluent West, the incidence of death from coronary heart disease has halved. This is certainly partly due to better emergency services, but it is considered to also strongly reflect the result of adult men consuming less animal fat in response to intensive public health awareness campaigns. Unfortunately, the younger people in the community are eating more and more animal fats because of their attraction to the 'fast food' franchises that sell food containing large amounts of animal fats. If this trend doesn't stop, people may again have much more arterial disease and cancer in decades to come.

Dr Dean Ornish, in his excellent book *Reversing Heart Disease*, described good research he did which showed that practising yoga in its widest sense, combined with a pure vegetarian diet, actually removed fatty plaques (atheroma) from the walls of the arteries and allowed the blood to once again flow through. In this way, the people studied avoided imminent coronary bypass surgery.[1] This is a very important observation, and bodes well for the future.

What sort of foods?

Although vegetarianism is not mandatory for yoga practitioners, many people who are practising yoga eat a vegetarian diet, and certainly all of the Satyananda ashrams throughout the world are vegetarian. It is more sattwic than the usual Western diet, and is generally better for the health and the heart.

We certainly need to eat better quality food that is fresher and free from chemicals, but also on the question of vegetarian diet, people who are agitated and anxious usually feel calmer if they eat less animal protein. I always recommend that people who have a disorder of the stress-tension-anxiety type try vegetarianism for at least three months to see how it suits them. This is a bit difficult for 'ordinary' people in the West; they don't know where to start, and eating vegetarian does require knowledge of what to eat. It is not just a matter of taking bits out of the usual Western diet. Many people come to ashrams to learn how to do it, others get the techniques from evening colleges and such places.

We need to be careful on the strict vegan diet (no animal products, even dairy) because some people don't absorb vitamin B12 very easily, so over a period of months or years they can develop anaemia. Even on a more liberal vegetarian diet, some people, usually of European ethnic origin, who don't absorb vitamin B12 well, need eggs from time to time to boost it up. Young women can also have a depletion of iron if their menstrual loss exceeds their intake. Generally, however, the average Indian-style vegetarian diet that includes a variety of grains, legumes, fruits, vegetables and dairy products is good for a lifetime.

Sugar

Sugar is consumed in vast quantities in both the East and the West. Many people easily get symptoms of hypoglycaemia because their bodies have difficulty handling large influxes of sugar into the bloodstream. The glucose in their blood rises to high levels quickly, the pancreas gland secretes excessive insulin, which transfers the glucose into the cells, and the blood level suddenly drops to a low level. This hypoglycaemia causes the person to become dizzy, tired, confused and emotionally unstable. Often the person learns to reverse this by consuming more sugar, and the whole vicious circle continues. Such people should avoid sugar, and eat more complex carbohydrates such as starch in natural cereals, and protein foods such as legumes and dairy products.

Carbonated soft drinks contain much more sugar than people realize, and in a dissolved, easily absorbed state. The extra sugar is there to overcome the effect of the fizz on the tongue and the phosphoric acid in some cola drinks. If you allow a soft drink to go 'flat', you will find it is so sweet that it is almost undrinkable.

Actually we don't need to take in any refined sugar at all, and are better if we don't. Try to get used to drinks and foods without the sweetness. You might not like it at first, but just consider it 'something else' and you might get to enjoy all those unsweetened foods and drinks.

Caffeine

Many people in all parts of the world consume caffeine in very large amounts. It is an addictive stimulant which keeps one awake, elevates the mood, and increases concentration and energy. However, because it causes secretion of adrenaline, too much of it can put the body into the *fight or flight mechanism,* with its tension, palpitations, inability to sleep, high blood pressure and feeling of anxiety. I have had patients over the years, who came with a diagnosis of anxiety disorder, but who when questioned admitted to drinking 15 or more cups of strong coffee per day. When they cut it down to only a few cups per day, their anxiety disorder 'miraculously' disappeared. Interestingly, one of them had been in psychotherapy with another therapist for some time for his anxiety, and nobody had thought about the coffee.

It's not just coffee though. The popular cola soft drinks and 'sports drinks' that are swallowed in vast amounts all over the world contain a lot of caffeine, so it is no wonder that tension, agitation and insomnia are so rife. They have large amounts of sugar, or aspartame (see below) as well, a formula for physical and emotional instability. The situation is even worse for children. I have seen mothers in supermarkets and stores who allowed a four-year-old child to choose his or her own soft drink from the refrigerator. Of course, the child chose the cola drink that is heavily advertised on TV. A can of that in such a small body is probably equivalent in an adult to about 5 cups of strong coffee with 13 or 14 spoonfuls of sugar, all at the one time!

We must also be aware of the time of day we take the stimulants. People often complain about difficulty sleeping, then tell me their habit is to drink a strong cup of coffee, or tea (which contains the stimulant theophylline), or chocolate (which contains the stimulant theobromine), just before going to bed. The best rule is: no stimulants after 3 pm, then sleep is actually assisted by the withdrawal effect from the substance.

Aspartame

This most commonly used artificial sweetener is a derivative of aspartic acid, which is one of the brain's excitatory neurotransmitter substances that produces activation and agitation of the central nervous system. To make matters worse, it is often taken in 'diet' soft drinks in company with lots of caffeine. No wonder the keen 'diet drink' people get so agitated and have a problem sleeping.

Alcohol

Alcohol has been prepared and consumed since time immemorial. As most people know, it relaxes the body and mind, and is used to break the ice at social gatherings because it dissolves people's inhibitions. Not only that, but recent reliable research from many parts of the world indicates that at the rate of about 2–3 standard drinks a day, it is associated with reduced illness of many types, and increased longevity as compared with non-drinkers.[2] This information may offend many people, and the results were not believed at first, but they have been repeated so many times and in so many places that they are now considered authentic. The scientists know that alcohol, by increasing the blood content of high-density lipoprotein, prevents fat forming in the walls of the arteries, and they suspect that this may be the mechanism of its benefit.

If that is so, we can get the same benefit from yoga by relieving stress, and reducing animal fats from our diet, or adopting a full vegetarian diet. Because the alcohol picture has a dark side too, of course. We all know that for some people it can be very addictive, leading them to irresponsible, self-destructive behaviour. The physical effects of drinking too much alcohol are also well known: high blood pressure, destruction of the liver, brain damage and general deterioration of the peripheral nervous system and other parts of the body.

Tobacco

The nicotine from tobacco is taken in various ways in different parts of the world. However, by far the most harmful form of nicotine intake is through smoking cigarettes. Nicotine is very addictive, so that people find it difficult to stop smoking, and that is reason enough to not begin in the first place. However, the smoke itself also contains chemicals that cause cancer of the lung and other parts of the body. It also destroys the tissues of the lungs, causing the fatal disease emphysema. It is said that heavy smokers, if they survive other smoking-related diseases, such as cancer, heart and blood vessel disease, will eventually develop emphysema, which they probably die from. In the West, over recent decades, public health promotion has led to a dramatic reduction in smoking by adult men, and an associated drop in lung cancer and emphysema. Unfortunately, women and young people seem to have missed the message, and are increasing their smoking.

Mind-altering drugs

These have also been taken for millennia, previously for religious purposes, but nowadays their use in the West has reached epidemic proportions. Maybe it is a response to people having lost their spiritual roots. If so, yoga has answers for them. The medical profession usually divides drugs that are taken into two groups: prescribed medications and self-administered. However, the distinction is not important because unless the person is under strict medical supervision, the disadvantages can be the same. One must be careful; drugs that alter mental or emotional functioning can be addictive in some people, and it is much better to substitute drug use with yoga practices.

At the worst end of the spectrum is the use of 'heavy' drugs, such as heroin and cocaine, which are associated with extremes of severe addiction and involvement with the 'drug scene' and criminal activity. Yoga should be made available to such people at various points on their 'detox' and rehabilitation path, and also to those in prisons.

Mercury

Mercury, a very toxic heavy metal used in the silver fillings (amalgam) in the teeth, certainly gets into the whole body. This is especially when the fillings are being placed there, when the old fillings are deteriorating and breaking down, and when they are being removed (unless great care is taken). Irrespective of claims made to the contrary, it was clearly demonstrated by many researchers in the 1970s that it does happen, and that it can have a very toxic effect. Fortunately amalgam is being phased out, and composite plastics are being used more and more nowadays. However, they are more expensive, and if you are poor, or in poorer societies,

167

you are likely to still get amalgams. Be advised, if you are to get a new filling in your teeth, insist that the dentist does not use amalgam.

PHYSICAL OUTPUT
WHAT COMES OUT OF THE BODY

These are the waste products. There is an old saying: "Constipation is the mother of all disease", and this can easily be realized when we consider how easily toxins can be absorbed through the bowel. It is also interesting that the main yoga practice used to treat diabetes is shankha-prakshalana. This consists of drinking two glasses of warm salty water, performing five postures that open the valves of the intestines, then repeating the process a number of times. This washes out the whole gastrointestinal tract. As we will see when we discuss the hatha yoga shatkarmas, yoga gives a lot of emphasis to purifying the body with these cleansing practices.

Remember anyway to drink plenty of water, get plenty of exercise and have plenty of roughage in the diet. There is another old saying: "An apple a day keeps the doctor away." This is very accurate because the fibre in an apple is pectin, which attracts and holds a lot of water in its descent through the bowel, and keeps the faeces soft so that it can pass easily. I recommend that my constipated patients have an apple or two each day, and it usually works for them. With plenty of roughage and water in the diet, and adequate exercise, the body can eliminate its waste products in faeces, urine and sweat.

MENTAL AND EMOTIONAL INTAKE

Right at the very foundation of evolving our personalities with yoga is the principle of eliminating from the uncon-scious mind the repressed material that has been holding us back. It is also the aim of the depth psychotherapies and

168

other aspects of psychology and psychiatry to improve our mental and emotional state. But what are we doing to stop a whole lot more 'garbage' from going into the memory stores, and dragging us back down again? Generally in the community – nothing! In addition, can we modify our lifestyle so that we take in high quality impressions that uplift us? There is an old song with the title 'Accentuate the Positive, Eliminate the Negative'. This is what we can try to do with what we take into our mind and emotional storehouse.

Negative intake

What content do we take in from TV, movies, internet, computer games, reading, music, etc.? Mentally, we take in impurities through all of the senses, especially sight and hearing, and continually add to the load of negative mental impressions (negative samskaras) we already have. It seems to be a part of modern life that from the moment we wake up in the morning, we must listen to the radio or watch the television set to fill our minds with all the horrible things people did to other people since the last time we listened or watched. Then as a recreation we go to the movies to watch more of the same. This is not even to mention the evil and degrading stuff that is thrust into people's sight nowadays on the internet. Then there's the company we keep; some people choose to associate with other people who regularly hurt them mentally and even physically. All this is harmful to us. We are supposed to be eliminating those negative samskaras, not adding to them. They give us negative attitudes, increase our level of anxiety and depression, and lower our level of evolution by dragging us down into tamas.

But does this intake really influence our thinking, emotions and behaviour? It certainly does. Many good psychology experiments have demonstrated this. For instance, children who observed adults expressing aggressive behaviour towards a large inflated doll were equally

169

aggressive towards it when it was their turn with it, whereas children who saw gentle behaviour were also gentle. This was repeated if the behaviour to the doll was seen on films. What about television at home? Children who had regularly watched violent cartoons were more aggressive in their interactions with their peers as compared with those who did not. Research done by L.D. Eron in 1972 showed that this aggression was continuing when they were re-investigated as 19-year-old youths ten years later.[3] Do you think maybe we should monitor the children's television watching and internet access, and our own too?

You may ask what the fuss is all about? Most people can watch a violent movie, and they don't go around beating up people on their way home from the theatre. It is a very important axiom in yoga that every impression (*samskara*) that goes into our mind leaves a permanent trace there. So every single samskara has its effect on our life from then on.

Consider this – inside our memory stores are *established categories* of memory about all kinds of influences in our life. For instance, what is your lifetime sum-total of memories about *mothers*, about *women* in general, about *fathers*, about *men* in general, about *lovers*, about the *honesty* of other people, etc., etc.? Each time you interact with one of these groups, more samskaras – positive or negative – will be added to the store and skew it in a positive or a negative direction. Keep adding more positive samskaras and the pool will become more and more positive; add the negative ones and it will become more and more negative. Strong emotionally loaded samskaras are even more powerful; for instance, violence or a loving caress will skew the category strongly.

So what? The problem is that the accumulated total of all the positive and negative samskaras about any one of these categories will influence the way you think, feel, behave and even perceive when you come in contact with an example of such a person or situation. For example, many of my male patients disliked women because of the memories of their past bad experiences with women. As a result their attitude towards women they met was bad, so the retaliation from the women just increased the negative impressions that were added to the category *'women'* in their memory banks – one of those vicious circles.

Age is also important. Older people with more life experiences have a much larger pool of memories, so each samskara adds just a little to the pool, but remember it *does* influence it. Young people have a smaller pool, so each addition of a new samskara influences the category a lot more and it will influence their responses in their life a lot more. Very young children especially must be protected from negative samskaras such as violence. We obviously can't avoid negative input ourselves, or completely protect our children from it, but we can strive to minimize it.

What about expressing anger to 'get it out of your system'? This is a fallacy. It has been clearly demonstrated that expressing anger only increases the likelihood of becoming angry later on. Anger becomes a *habit,* not a cleansing. This supports the contention of Sage Patanjali in the *Yoga Sutras* that:

> When the mind is disturbed by passions, one should practise pondering their opposites.

So the principle behind purification is not only working to eliminate the physical and mental impurities we already have, but also adjusting our life so that we take in as few new negative impressions as possible.

Positive intake

How do we 'accentuate the positive' intake? Mainly by choosing our company – human, viewing, listening and environmental. We looked at some of the corrupting factors out there that we can avoid. There are also good influences that will help us, and when we start selecting what we view, what we listen to, and compatible environments, we find more and more positive influences.

Satsang is a yogic term which means keeping company with saints. There are not many saints around these days, but a good second best is to spend our time with other people who are on the path of evolving themselves. This is one of the reasons people choose to live in yoga ashrams. If we can associate with a spiritual master at the same time, the positive process is greatly accelerated. Another way to improve our intake and start another of those virtuous circles is to behave morally and ethically to other people and to ourselves.

This brings us to our next discussion, the question of ethics and personal wellbeing – the yamas and niyamas of raja yoga. (We will consider the other six limbs of raja yoga when we discuss the yoga techniques.)

12

Raja Yoga Lifestyle Principles

In summary these are the self-restraints *(yamas)* and personal codes *(niyamas)*.

Self-restraints *(yamas)* – *harmonize one's social interactions*
- Non-violence – *ahimsa* – non-harmful intent
- Truthfulness – *satya* – straight and true with self and others
- Honesty – *asteya* – including non-stealing, results from being non-acquisitive
- Non-possessiveness – *aparigraha* – a result of non-attachment
- Continence – *brahmacharya* – 'to walk with Brahma', continence in sex and other desire states.

Personal codes *(niyamas)* – *harmonize one's inner feelings*
- Cleanliness – *shaucha* – purity of all koshas and one's environment
- Contentment – *santosha* – happy with life and its problems
- Austerity – *tapas* – simplicity of life – developing endurance, stamina, willpower
- Self-study – *swadhyaya* – self-observation, analysis and knowledge
- Cultivation of faith – *Ishwara pranidhana* – faith in a higher reality, also surrender of oneself and one's actions to the higher power.

According to Sage Patanjali in the *Yoga Sutras*, the yamas and niyamas help us to evolve ourselves. Some would say that trying to observe them completely can cause us more stress, guilt, etc., and make matters worse. Swami Satyananda in *Four Chapters on Freedom* (his commentary on the 'Yoga Sutras') is quite clear what to do about this. He wrote:

> The intrinsic nature of all human beings is to be truthful, honest, good and compassionate. Anything done to the contrary, though appearing to be a manifestation of the individual's true nature, is therefore an act which has arisen through circumstances in life, perhaps poverty, mistreatment by other people, and so on. Consciously that individual feels he is only doing what comes naturally, but subconsciously it is a different story. Conflict occurs in the subconscious realms and this causes mental disturbances which we feel, but don't know the cause.

> A conflict arises between what one actually does, and what the subconscious really wants to do. In this way mental problems occur. Therefore, the yamas and niyamas are applicable to everyone. Even if we abide by them to the slightest extent, this is a definite step in the right direction. Don't aim further than you are able; tread slowly and gently.

In other words, go easy on yourself, you are not perfect yet. But keep the yamas and niyamas in mind and realize the peace of mind that can come from them, because observing them can prevent disquiet of the mind. How?

1. At the basic level, if we have hurt people, or lied to them, or cheated them, or sexually exploited them, they are just waiting in the background. It may be that they just rebuff us later, or there may be deep and painful vengeance when we least expect it and, according to Murphy's law, at the worst possible time.

2. If the hurting, lying or cheating, etc., has not been found out, there is the continuous suspense in the back of one's mind that it will be revealed.
3. There is always the disquiet of our higher levels of consciousness knowing what we have done, and it just sits there in some part of the mind.

This is what Sage Patanjali was getting at. In the meditation context it is not the morality of the thing that is important, it is what it does to one's state of mind. It is a potent source of *vrittis* that disturb us.

But it is difficult at the start to observe the yamas and niyamas. Swami Niranjan has even said that for many people asanas, pranayamas, pratyahara and dharana should be practised first nowadays, so we have some clarity and balance when we start on the yamas and niyamas. Of course, there are also many people who do practise these throughout their lives, because it just comes naturally to them; there are a lot of very ethical and refined people out there.

What can we do about the yamas and niyamas?
1. First know about them.
2. Realize how they can bring peace of mind and help us to evolve.
3. Then get the witness working and watching our thoughts, emotions and behaviour. At first we will usually recognize the breach after it has happened, but after a while we will see the temptation before it happens.
4. When we recognize the pattern before it happens, we can ask ourselves questions such as:
   "Here I am getting angry again – the old revenge game, do I really want to continue it?"
   "I'm just about to tell another lie . . . do I really want to?"
   "Do I really need this thing I'm striving for?"
   "Do I really need all these things in my life?"
   "Do I really need to get tangled up in this sexual (or other emotionally charged) exploit?"

RAJA YOGA – SELF-RESTRAINTS (YAMAS)

These are self-restraints and social codes – yogic self-control; they harmonize one's social and internal interactions.

Why moral codes in a work on meditation? To quote Swami Satyananda again from *Four Chapters on Freedom*:

> The yamas are designed to harmonize one's social interactions, and the niyamas are intended to harmonize one's inner feelings. All the rules, yamas and niyamas, are designed to reduce friction between one's outer actions and inner attitudes. There is a two-way relationship: the mind stimulates external actions, and external actions stimulate the mind. If the external actions are not harmonious, then the mind will be disturbed. Conversely, a disturbed mind will tend to produce disharmonious acts.

> The rules are not easy to apply, but even limited application will lead to greater peace of mind. Perfect application can only arise with self-realization, but we can continue to improve as our life goes on.

Non-violence (*ahimsa*)

This is the feeling of non-violence or even non-hostility towards all things. When we start to become aware of it, we can detect it more in our thoughts, emotions, desires, feelings, motivation, ambitions, words and deeds. Then our actions are more frequently done without harmful intent. We should just observe these tendencies, learn from them, and decide not to repeat them. Don't get into the 'guilt game' – that is violence to ourselves. But what about guilt? If we realize we have the guilt tendency, find out why. Who, in our past, originally used guilt to manipulate us? Get into meditation and ask the unconscious mind who and how; see what answers come.

As we give more attention to others and less to ourselves, we increase our awareness and reduce the ego. As we give more attention to the non-harming of others and caring for them, we become more compassionate. It keeps it in our mind. We get to a state where we don't even react to negative input from others.

As one develops ahimsa, one detects one's violence at subtle levels, but also that there is less violence around. Sage Patanjali observed this when he wrote, "On being firmly established in ahimsa, there is abandonment of hostility in one's vicinity." Swami Satyananda wrote in *Four Chapters on Freedom*:

> When one is established in ahimsa, there develops a kind of magnetism around the person that influences everybody who approaches. The person becomes free of a very dangerous, evil complex, that of violence and hostility.

Ahimsa evolves the tamasic and rajasic qualities of the personality into the sattwic, so it evolves the qualities of our anahata chakra system. At the same time, as we evolve anahata by any other yogic means, it makes it easier for us to experience ahimsa – it just becomes natural for us. Then when we are at the sattwic level we *become* ahimsa simply because it is 'not natural' for us to hurt others. This is another typical example of the breaking of vicious circles and the development of virtuous circles that occurs as we evolve in yoga.

Truthfulness (*satya*)

This also involves our thoughts, words and deeds. It is commitment to truth, being truthful at all these levels. Many people believe they are lying and getting away with it; they are not. Lies create strain and fear of discovery, even unconsciously, and disturb the mind.

There is a bonus in the truth too. If you are a truthful person, people trust you, so your relationships are sincere and more harmonious. Remember that others know at some level of their being (of which they are often not aware) when you are being truthful.

If you lie, other people know. If they decide to join your deceit, that's up to them, but if they do, maybe they are not the kind of people you want as confederates. Another problem with lying is that we have to continue telling lies to support the ones that went before, and most people don't have a good enough memory to remember the ones that went before; it can become very complicated. The old saying goes something like this: "Oh what a tangled web we weave when we set out to deceive."

But truth should not be used to intentionally hurt someone. We should always try to speak the kind truth, *to* other people and *about* other people. When we are speaking about other people, we should try to stay positive about them – otherwise it may be best not to say anything.

We should be sincere and true to ourselves as well. If we deceive ourselves with denial and rationalization, it 'muddies' our thinking and we can't be clear with ourselves. If we can be true to ourselves about ourselves, we can clear the mental blocks that are holding us back from realizing our real potentials.

What about 'diplomacy'? Does this mean that lying for a just cause is OK? "Do you like my new dress, darling?" What do you say? What do we do when satya and ahimsa come into conflict, when telling even the kind truth is likely to hurt the other person? There may be no answer to that question that applies at all times, but one thing is certain – as we evolve the qualities of our compassion and love for others, our answer is likely to be better, the outcome from it happier.

What if one is in trouble? Sometimes it takes courage to firmly tell the truth in the face of adamant antagonism. This is the big test of our satya. Where does the courage come from? There is a clue to this in the English language; it is the slang word for courage: 'guts'! Manipura chakra. It emanates from a strong, evolved manipura chakra and includes the power and self-esteem inherent in that. This then becomes another virtuous circle we develop with yoga. The more we have the courage to tell the truth, the more the power and self-esteem qualities of our manipura system grow. As this happens, either in this way or through any other route of evolving manipura, truth becomes more and more part of our nature. We just naturally "tell the truth and face the music".

But should we always tell the truth even if by doing so we will support an evil influence? Should you have admitted to the Gestapo that you knew where the fleeing Jewish escapees were hiding? Should you give helpful information to a violent autocrat? If the law of the land is corrupt and wrong, should you support it in court? Hopefully the decisions you have to make about truth in your lives will be kinder than these, because here we have another conflict between satya and ahimsa. In the opinion of this writer we must first honour ahimsa and try to prevent harm.

We find with all of these moral questions that our best decisions are obvious to us in ordinary everyday situations. However, when we get into extreme situations, we get caught in dilemmas and conflicts of principles, and the decisions are certainly not obvious. The yogic answer to this is to keep evolving up into the sattwic levels where our decisions will not be corrupted by our own mental 'garbage', and their quality will be influenced by our higher information and motives. In addition, we can often have a 'big picture' experience that puts the dilemma in a new perspective, and helps us to make the correct decision.

Honesty (*asteya*)

This means not stealing other people's possessions, but it also means internal honesty, simplicity and sincerity – honesty at all levels. It means not cheating or manipulating people for our own gain. It also means not justifying our dishonesty by tricky excuses and using the laws of society. There is certainly some relationship between the laws of a truly democratic country and morality, ethics and equality. However, they are certainly not identical. Some lawyers

179

operate in the spaces between them, but if we are honest with ourselves, we can't.

Honesty comes from an attitude of non-acquisitiveness. Obviously, if we are non-acquisitive, there is no need for us to acquire other people's things, so there is no question of dishonesty. But if my children are hungry and I have no money, I will be acquisitive, whereas if we have enough food, I don't need to be. So at one level it is about being able to differentiate between needs and wants – needs and ambitions in the SWAN principle, which we will discuss in Chapter 15.

The cynics would certainly laugh derisively at this principle of asteya, and say that dishonesty does pay, that many dishonest people live a long, comfortable and apparently happy life. But Sage Patanjali clearly states in the *Yoga Sutras* (2:31) (from *Four Chapters on Freedom* by Swami Satyananda Saraswati):

> When practised universally without exception to birth, place, time and circumstances they (the yamas) become great disciplines.

He is referring to the peace of mind in our lives that comes from honesty, but there is more than this. Many people who believe in reincarnation, like Sage Patanjali, would support this contention by adding that even if Nemesis doesn't seem to pounce on us for our dishonesty, this is not our only life. For most people there are many lives to come, and plenty of time for such karma and the people involved in it to catch up with us.

Asteya applies through all levels of our being. At the level of living, it means living simply and sincerely. At the level of vitality, it means not 'stealing' other people's energy. Some people have very low vitality, and they have the ability to literally suck the energy out of other people, depleting their energy in the process. (This is thought to be the origin of the human vampire myth, and it is interesting that in depleting the victim's energy, they turn the victim into a 'vampire' – at least temporarily – just as it says in the stories.) These people should practise yoga to boost their own vitality.

At the level of manas, asteya means, for instance, not stealing other people's ideas, and interrupting any dishonest thoughts when we realize them. At the level of buddhi, it can mean not stealing other people's intellectual property. Such plagiarism is not fair to the person who created the material, and deprives the thief of the enlightening opportunity to find out for themselves. In addition, people may discover the fraud, and then disgrace follows. It is a sheer waste for our higher reasoning power to serve behaviour that lowers us instead of utilizing it for our evolution.

Ultimately, it is the quality of *non-acquisitiveness* that makes it natural for us to follow asteya. It is a quality of the mooladhara chakra system. People who are evolved up in the sattwic levels of mooladhara do not feel the basic insecurity that drives others to compulsively acquire material things. They are content with what they have, and are more likely to be generous with the material things they have than wanting to acquire more.

Honesty can be a difficult moral dilemma when faced with real need, but in general if we practise honesty in our lives, we will have more peace of mind. This will augment our feelings of security, which will help to evolve the qualities of mooladhara chakra and in turn increase our basic feeling of security and non-acquisitiveness – another virtuous circle.

Non-possessiveness (*aparigraha*)

This is really the result of non-attachment, and just like asteya, it is a function of the degree of evolvement of the mooladhara chakra system. Our drive to acquire material possessions and our urge to hoard them result from the insecurity inherent in low evolution of mooladhara. When we can rise out of that level, we care for our possessions or the people in our lives, but we are not addicted to them.

It is not just material possessions to which we become attached and possessive; it can be all the things of our life such as people, roles, titles, social positions, habitual

181

thinking patterns, favourite emotions, personal opinions, ideas, behaviour patterns, all sorts of desires and cravings, all aspects of our ego, etc.

The problem here is the mental and emotional chaos that results. If our basic insecurity drives us to want to possess and hold all these things, they come with 'strings attached' and usually cause more problems than they solve. What are the 'strings'?

If we don't get them, we are discontented at least, maybe even angry. If we do get them, we become frightened we might lose them or that they might be damaged. Some people have vast amounts of wealth, but they are unhappy and frightened because they are so attached to it. As Antoine de Rivarol said: "There are men who gain from their wealth only the fear of losing it."

The secret of dealing with our attachments to all these things is first of all to realize it. How do we do that? By recognizing our emotional reactions to being deprived of them or to the threat of losing them. Next we have to deal with these attachments. As with the other yamas, as we practise yoga and start to deal with our problems in these spheres, the qualities of the relevant chakra systems evolve. When this begins to happen, we set in train another virtuous circle and the improvement becomes a chain reaction.

Continence (*brahmacharya*)

This literally means 'one who is established in the higher reality – moving on the path of Brahma – walking in the light'.

Continence in sex and other desire states is at the basis of it, from the realization that indulgence in the activities involving desires, including sexuality, reduces the prana which can be used for spiritual evolvement. It depends on the person's stage of development.

Maybe continence makes sense, but what about celibacy? In 1975, when Swami Satyananda was presiding at the Yoga Convention in Colombia, he was asked, "For spiritual life should we be celibate?" He answered, "Of course not; celibacy is against the laws of nature!" I was amazed then to hear a yoga master say that, but I'm not now. I realize that he was speaking to that particular audience of mainly married mums and dads. It was certainly against the laws of their nature.

As mentioned in the discussion on the evolution of the aspects of the chakra systems, there is a time in one's evolution when celibacy is just natural. We evolve from tamas where there is little sexuality because of the inertia, to more rajasic-tamas where sexuality is just an animal lust. Then comes evolvement through rajas where sexuality finds appropriate but imperative expression, to rajasic-sattwic when it ceases to be such a compulsive drive but is still very fulfilling, and to high sattwa when it is no longer necessary.

The lower down people are in their evolution when they take on celibacy, the more stress it will produce, especially if the swadhisthana system is quite active. Try it in rajas and the suppression is so strong that either it causes a lot of tension, or it breaks out into overt sexual activities. We are seeing this nowadays in the scandals involving 'celibate' clergy. Was it appropriate for them to take vows of celibacy when they were just inexperienced young men?

Celibacy is a state of being that just becomes part of the person's evolutionary progress. The closer we 'walk with Brahma', the more natural celibacy is. Certainly it is said that to attain the higher states of meditation we need powerful levels of energy, and at that point the yogis recommend celibacy. This is probably because by the time we reach that level, it is natural for us to be celibate anyway and it won't cause the stress and tension. In addition, the person is usually living a non-voluptuous lifestyle, and working so hard for the benefit of others that the sexual drive is sublimated.

There are other people who take easily to celibacy because their swadhisthana system is relatively inactive; some people don't have much going on there at all. As a matter of fact, this applies to the desires of the other chakra systems too; people with low activity are not 'bothered' by those temptations. As William Blake, the English poet, humorously wrote: "Those who restrain desire do so because theirs is weak enough to be restrained."

Remember also that another interpretation of brahmacharya is 'continence' rather than complete celibacy. In this context discretion in all activities which involve such emotional involvement with other people can avoid stress just by virtue of saving us from a multiplicity of emotional connections. The committed relationship makes sense; promiscuousness can really complicate the lives of everyone concerned, and lead to stress.

RAJA YOGA – PERSONAL CODES (NIYAMAS)

These are personal codes – inner observances and disciplines. Whereas the yamas were about our relationships with others and our social interactions generally, the niyamas are to do with our inner personal life. They harmonize our inner feelings and create discipline in our inner life.

Cleanliness (*shaucha*)

This is purity at all levels – cleanliness of the body, external and internal, neatness and order in our environment, and purification of the mind. The hatha yoga shatkarmas are designed to help with this in all these dimensions.

It means cleanliness in all its areas, especially physical and mental, as pointed out in the *Yoga Sutras*. In most yogic writings the emphasis is on cleaning the physical impurities, such as washing the skin, inner washing such as shankhaprakshalana, cleaning teeth, etc. The mental purifications are of course the elimination of samskaras from the mind, and form the crux of the early phases of meditation practices. But the purity also extends to one's environment. How clean and neat is one's living space? How tidy is one's office? How organized is one's schedule?

Just as important as cleansing is the prevention of taking in impurities. Physically, what is the quality of the food, drink

184

and air we take in? Is the food full of animal fats, salt and sugar? Is it contaminated with chemicals and depleted of essential vitamins and minerals? What is the quality of the air we breathe? Is there a way we can take in pure food and pure drink? Is there a way we can live in a place where the air is pure, instead of in polluted cities? Can we stay away from such things as cigarette smoke and car exhausts? Even an old pillow can be heavily contaminated with mould and dust mite faeces, and we breathe that air all night.

Mentally, the impurities we take in through all the senses add to the load of negative samskaras we already have. We are supposed to be eliminating these, not adding to them. They give us negative attitudes, increase our level of anxiety and depression, and lower our level of evolution.

So the principle behind shaucha is not only working to eliminate the physical and mental impurities we already have, but adjusting our life so that we take in as few as possible. It then leads to, and is amplified by, a positive view of our world and the individuals in it; positive sensible thinking, attitudes and discrimination; positive feelings and emotions; and positive, kind, friendly social interactions – another virtuous circle.

The yoga system also emphasizes purifying the mind because concentration and meditation are impossible while the clutter of the lower unconscious mind keeps intervening in the meditation process. In addition, while it is present, it causes mental, emotional and psychosomatic illness.

Contentment (*santosha*)

This is being satisfied with what we have. Remember the saying: "Wealth is not having a lot, but being content with what we have." This develops as we evolve; our demands become fewer, and our life becomes simpler, so we are more contented. We develop the ability to maintain serenity even when things are difficult. There is another saying: "Serenity is not freedom from the storm, but peace amid the storm." We become more secure so we don't need possessions to soothe our anxiety. We are more joyous so the world around us is a happier place. We have a sense of mastery in our lives and more vitality to function efficiently, so our self-esteem is high. We are able to give and receive love, and to communicate well with people, so our relationships with them are more fulfilling.

Austerity (*tapas*)

As we live simply we become more able to cope with hardships without negative reaction. According to some yogis, enduring difficulties and hardships can give us confidence, stamina and willpower. They say that the more adversity we know we can tolerate, the more peace of mind we have because we don't fear adversity happening. Some yogis actually impose hardships on themselves so that having already endured them, if they occur later, they don't disturb their equipoise. This is a powerful path for some, but others have to be careful because it can also become a big ego-trip for premature saints. Buddha had practised tapas for years before he woke up to the fact that he was getting nowhere. It was after he stopped it all that he became enlightened.

As 'amateurs', we can start with small austerities such as fasting, spending more time alone, observing silence (*mouna*), etc. It is said that at an advanced point on the yogic path for some aspirants, real hardships become necessary to strengthen their system for the rigorous experiences ahead. However, for the average person on this yoga path of evolving the personality, they are not yet necessary. For one who is accustomed to the luxuries of today's affluent societies, just to endure the modest hardships of the simple life is a good start.

Self-study (*swadhyaya*)

This is self-observation, analysis and knowledge of our own personality – becoming aware of our strengths, weaknesses, ambitions and needs. We can be helped on this path by external aids such as books, stories about saints, masters, geniuses, etc., lectures, and discussions by masters and other experts. They are used in conjunction with the other yoga practices, which allow us to become more and more 'the witness'. We become more able to 'stand aside' and observe our own perceptions of the world, our attitudes about it, and our thoughts, emotions and behaviour. The ability of a person to do this is necessary for any type of therapy in psychology, and is called 'insight'. As the yoga practices increase insight, they are very valuable if used as an adjunct to Western clinical psychology. Yoga can also stand alone as a way to evolve our full potentials.

Cultivation of faith (*Ishwara pranidhana*)

This is not only faith in the existence of a higher reality, but ultimately, as Sage Patanjali said, "complete resignation to it." This includes the aspects of karma and bhakti yogas (see Chapters 13 and 14) in which one develops the sense that it is not I who am performing the action, but that it is being done through me, by a higher power. Then one starts to realize that the work just flows, that everything needed to do the work comes along, and that what seemed to be coincidences or even problems are actually the divine plan in action. Then another virtuous circle develops, because the realization of grace increases our faith, which raises us to further levels of non ego involvement – non-doership – the attitude of only being the *instrument*, not the doer.

Four ways of life

The 'big four' branches of yoga are considered to be: raja yoga, karma yoga, bhakti yoga and jnana yoga. In this chapter we discussed the raja yoga lifestyle recommendations; in the next three chapters we will deal with the other three. All are powerful ways of improving our lifestyle and enhancing our evolvement. For this reason they are very important and deserve our closest attention. If we can incorporate just a few of these principles into our way of life, it will be of immense benefit to us and improve all areas of our existence.

13

The Karma Yoga Life

The yoga of dynamic meditation

Karma yoga is the yoga of action, but it is action done in a special way. The word *karma* is derived from the Sanskrit root *kri* (to do or to make); it means 'action', but in some respects karma is also the results of our actions – we reap what we sow. Then when we add the word 'yoga', it means that the action is done with meditative awareness. So karma yoga is meditation 'on the job', as some would say 'eyes open' meditation. That is the first and principal criterion of karma yoga; we are 'out there' doing things with clear awareness, but we are doing so with an awareness that is as one-pointed as it is in meditation with the eyes closed.

Actually we are always in action, even when we are apparently doing nothing. At least our minds are in action, and at some level we are still affecting the objects or people about whom we are thinking. Even asleep we dream, and even in deep sleep we are interacting at some level. So the yogis say that if we are always in action, we had better act in the right way. In Chapter 3 of the *Bhagavad Gita* we see:

> Verily none can ever remain for even a moment without performing action. (v. 5)

> He who, restraining the organs of action, sits thinking in his mind of the sense-objects, he of deluded understanding is called a hypocrite. (v. 6)

But whosoever, controlling the senses by the mind, O Arjuna, engages his organs of action in karma yoga, without attachment, he excels. (v. 7)

THE COMPONENTS OF KARMA YOGA

1. Meditative awareness

The right way to perform action is karma yoga, which we do with an inner attitude of meditative awareness – "controlling the senses by the mind", as Sri Krishna said, which increases the level of our awareness of the whole situation and ourselves. This is a typical example of how the practices of yoga that we perform impact directly on our life. The meditation practice we do with our eyes closed trains us so that we can then take those skills out into the world, so the mental state continues with our eyes open. We get many benefits such as:

Concentration on the job helps us to work more efficiently, so the work goes more smoothly. As well as that, if I am concentrating completely on the work at hand, I forget about me, and about all those worries and resentments – I eliminate the old internal monologue. People who master this ability of total concentration also realize happiness in the process. Most people seek happiness by pursuing pleasure, and find that they get farther and farther from the happiness; then when they least expect it, there it is, as they concentrate on helping others.

Observation. During the process of observing both you and me, I realize the reactive patterns of thinking, emotion, and behaviour of myself and of you. "What are my responses to this work, what are my responses to you, what are your attitudes towards me, what are your responses to what I am doing?" We can learn a lot about ourselves and other people this way, and we evolve in the process. In addition, observation of what is going on as the work unfolds keeps us on track.

Expansion of our awareness is a bonus of the meditation practices. It gives us a bigger picture of what we are doing, which allows us to make much better decisions. Don't underestimate the expansion of awareness that occurs as a result of any of the forms of meditation. A military general and staff have to make strategic and tactical decisions in the course of a battle. If they are on the ground, their information will be limited to what they can see, and maybe radio communications. However, if they are up in a helicopter, well above the whole battlefield, they will have a big picture of where everybody is and how the battle is going, and they will be able to make better decisions. This is a concrete example, but in subtle ways it applies in our everyday life too as our overall viewpoint of life expands.

Witness position. This ability to observe without becoming emotionally involved protects us from getting entangled in the 'dramas' around us, and at the same time allows us to make better decisions about any crises that come our way.

2. Service

The next principle of karma yoga is that of service *(seva)* where our actions are done *in* the world *for* the world and for the benefit of others. The first thing we notice when we do this is that our relationships with other people become more positive and harmonious. In addition, if we are working for the world or for the benefit of others, we are working in concert with our higher self – our unitive aspect – and that produces immediate harmony and tuning in to our higher levels of evolvement. Moreover, if we are working for others, we have no personal expectations, so we don't have the disappointments that are caused by unmet expectations. Thus we avoid the stress that can hold us down in the lower levels.

Still, the idea of selfless service in karma yoga can be difficult to get across to people. Their receptivity to it really depends on the level of their evolution. If we broach the subject to someone who is still struggling in the hell of tamas, the whole idea seems ridiculous to them. The person at the rajasic level will also have trouble seeing the sense in giving of ourselves in this way without getting plenty in return. But the idea immediately appeals to people who are already living at a fairly sattwic level, and they can see how living our lives in the karma yoga way can help us evolve.

3. Non attachment

What are the effects of non-attachment on the results of our activities? Chapter 3 of the *Bhagavad Gita* tells us:

> As ignorant men act from attachment to action so should the wise act without attachment, wishing the welfare of the world. (v. 25)

> Attachment and aversion for the objects of the senses abide in the senses; let none come under their sway; for they are his foes. (v. 34)

What do we become attached to? Our attraction *(raga)* to all those sensual objects of our desires, and our repulsion *(dwesha)* from those things we don't want. We can relate this to chakra qualities such as:

Mooladhara – attracted to external sources of security, money and possessions; repelled by threatening situations and potential losses of money and possessions.

Swadhisthana – attracted to sensual pleasures, including sex, situations and people who give us enjoyment; repelled by discomforts and pain, and 'depressing' situations.

Manipura – attracted to situations that give us power and control, and boost our self-esteem; repelled by threats to our power and control, and situations of embarrassment and shame.

Anahata – attracted to situations from which we can 'get love'; repelled by situations where we are not 'getting love' or are getting rejection.

Vishuddhi – attracted to avenues for communication; repelled by solitude, loneliness and boredom.

Ajna – attracted to sources of information (usually for use in our control); repelled by situations where we don't have the information we desire.

There are two questions wanting to be asked here:
1. "What's wrong with those things we are attracted to?" Answer: Nothing, as long as they are helpful for the work we have to do. But they are not lasting; life takes them from us, and then the problem becomes our *attachment* to them – our addiction to them. The pain from that is what holds us back, and so we have to be eternally vigilant.
2. "Isn't it natural to be repelled by negative things such as having our money taken, suffering discomforts and pain, powerlessness, unrequited love, boredom, lack of information, etc?" Answer: Yes, not many people enjoy those, but they occur in each person's life. Once again the problem is our emotional attachment to avoiding these experiences. If the avoidance becomes addictive, we are likely to get caught up in all sorts of addictive activities and compulsive escapism; then our service to the world and our own evolvement fall in a heap.

Non-attachment is an anti-stressor, and helps us to evolve because if we are not attached to something:
· We are not afraid to lose it, so fear decreases. Some people with a lot of money care for it but are not attached to it, so they can live a contented life, often using the money for good purposes.
· If we do lose it, there is not that automatic disappointment, anger, etc. Swami Niranjan said, "The reverse of attachment is compassion *(karuna)*."

The man of renunciation, pervaded by purity, intelligent, and with his doubts cut asunder, does not hate a disagreeable work nor is he attached to an agreeable one. (*Bhagavad Gita* 18:10)

4. Non-expectation

Undertaking activity without seeking personal reward and performing actions without craving results is really related to non-expectation. Non-expectation is non-attachment to future results, so the principles that apply there apply here also. But must we have NO expectations at all? If we are doing a worthwhile job, we will have some expectations of a positive outcome of the job itself, but even then we have to be flexible enough in those expectations to accept the inevitable changes life throws at us along the way.

But what about preoccupation with 'personal' expectations and rewards? What are the results of that? Think about the attractions and repulsions that stem from the qualities of the chakras. Alternatively, if we just work for the welfare of the world and other individuals and for the sake of the work itself, we will have peace of mind. "Don't expect anything, then if you don't get anything you won't be disappointed."

"Shouldn't I expect some reward? Surely if I need the money, I can expect to be paid for my work." Of course, if we need to be paid so that we can support ourselves and maybe the family, this should be established as agreements or even contracts at the beginning, but still we can devote our selfless attention to the work.

Then in the process of giving of ourselves, something strange often happens. Many people who embark on the road of karma yoga find that they start to receive abundant payment. This may be because the people they work for appreciate their efforts, but it may also be because this is part of the natural *law of karma*: we do indeed reap what we sow.

> Verily it is not possible for an embodied being to abandon actions entirely; but he who relinquishes the rewards of actions is verily called a man of renunciation. (*Bhagavad Gita* 18:11)

So although it is not possible for embodied beings to renounce action, it is certainly possible to renounce the results of the action.

4. Appropriate life direction (*swadharma*)
One should remain aware of one's own personal *dharma* in the sense of both one's *appropriate life direction* and the *duty* that comes from it.

Therefore, perform your bounden duty, because action is superior to inaction. (*Bhagavad Gita* 4:8)

There are two points here.

1. *Appropriate life direction*: Because of the qualities of our own personal nature, there is a way of life that is most appropriate to us, and the closer we can follow that direction, the happier and more uplifting life will be. This applies to all of us. Many people are in the wrong place, in the wrong job, in the wrong relationships – they are 'square pegs in round holes', and do not fit comfortably.

2. *Duty*: Each way of life contains within it certain obligations and duties, and they must be performed. For instance, because of Arjuna's 'princely' and rajasic nature, he was 'cut out' to be a military officer, and the *duty* inherent in that is the necessity to fight. Others are naturally inclined to be doctors, so their *duty* involves caring for the health of their patients.

In *Yoga Darshan* Swami Niranjan describes this point and karma yoga in general:

Consider . . . every action to be a duty. Do your duty, for action is superior to inaction. When action is performed with the idea of duty, it produces a very deep experience of bhakti, surrender, belief, trust and faith in a higher nature, a higher reality guiding us. This duty is to be understood in relation to one's individual, social, global and universal dharma.

When one develops the awareness of dharma as an inherent commitment, duty or obligation towards other beings, then one develops a giving or helping nature. Often people talk about and believe in giving a helping hand to others, but our actions, which may seem outwardly like helping, do not necessarily convey the same feeling to others. Often even the desire to help others carries with it some thought of gain or profit. Helping others is in itself a dharma. We should not be restricted by the idea of some kind of personal gain.

Initially, the practice of karma yoga is difficult because to combine the concepts of efficiency, non-expectation, equanimity, egolessness, renunciation and duty in one action is difficult. The thrust of karma yoga is to have these concepts combined in one thought, in one action, in one moment. Once these different ideas are combined, then we can say that we are practising karma yoga.

However, until then, we can do the best we can. In the workplace or at home with the family, when we are with other people, and indeed even when we are alone, relating to ourselves, we can remember to apply the karma yoga principles. Then over time it will become second nature in all our actions, bringing peace of mind. Karma yoga clears the mind of phobias, insecurities and complexes, and makes it steadier for further practices and for evolving in this life. The ultimate state is total serenity in the midst of intense action.

6. Positive attitude

This is looking on the positive side of all life's activities. Some people are optimists who customarily see the positive side of things; some people are pessimists who usually see things negatively. What is the cause of the difference? According to yogic thinking, some of the causes of differences between these people would be:

1. If there is imbalance in the flow of the air through the nostrils, or any other cause of ongoing dominance of one side of the brain, a person can get stuck in either optimism or pessimism – either of which can be inappropriate.
2. Deep unconscious fears caused by emotional trauma in the past can cause a person to be hypervigilant and always meet new situations with pessimism.
3. Sheer habit, usually copied from a pessimistic parent.

All of these are eminently reversible by yoga, and if a person is habitually pessimistic, they should rectify the situation to try to get a sensible, balanced but positive attitude.

We can strive to bring forth our positive attitudes while noticing, but not getting entangled in, the negative ones. One general way to do this is to 'count your blessings'. If things are difficult, remember, "It could be worse; think of the good things in this situation."

Swami Niranjan's question is: "When you see a rose, do you see the beautiful flower or the thorns? The choice is yours."

7. Efficiency

We may define efficiency as 'doing the work as cleanly, neatly, quickly, economically and effectively as possible'. Inefficiency causes problems, problems cause stress, and stress keeps us down in the more tamasic levels where the work becomes even less efficient – another tamasic vicious circle. So do it right in the first place.

If we are really practising karma yoga as 'meditation in action', the efficiency will come automatically because the *concentration* on the job helps us to work efficiently. In addition, *observation* of what is going on keeps us on track as the work unfolds. The *expansion* of awareness that develops with meditation allows us to observe the whole event or situation, and this is necessary for efficiency, Finally, in the *witness position* we are not diverted from the job by the emotional 'sideshows' going on around us.

One trick is to try to make the job perfect – but do it as a game, not as a compulsive imperative. While doing this keep watching your reactions.

8. Equanimity

This is balance of mind in success or failure, praise or criticism, fame or disgrace, etc.

As Swami Niranjan wrote in *Yoga Darshan*:

> If our mind becomes disturbed by failure and success, then we swing like a pendulum, from one side to the other, from a positive and optimistic approach during

success, to a negative and pessimistic approach during failure. This swing of the mind from success to failure and failure to success is very disturbing and distracting.

It certainly turns our efforts at karma yoga into failure.

In the *Bhagavad Gita* (4:22) Sri Krishna describes the person with equanimity as:

Content with what comes to him without effort, free from the pairs of opposites and envy, even-minded in success and failure; though acting, he is not bound.

But it is not easy to maintain equanimity. We need to reduce and eventually abandon the desires of attachment, the desire for results, the desire for achievement, the desire for reputation, social position, status, money – all the things that stroke our ego. For this reason, in order to maintain the necessary mental balance, it is necessary for most of us to be practising the other yogas as well.

9. Non-ego involvement

Non-doership is the attitude of only being the *instrument*, not the doer – the realization that we are not indispensable. People find this very difficult because we like our ego rewards, but when this is working properly, it is a wonderful feeling; the work just flows along guided by a higher force without our selfish ego blocking it.

Some people say that what appears as divine grace is just coincidence, but when it is really flowing it happens so consistently that the odds of so many coincidences happening in a row are astronomical. Others say it is caused by one's positive frame of mind attracting the good fortune, but sometimes the train of circumstances that leads to the result has started many years ago, long before the task at hand was even thought of. Such experiences develop the sense of non-doership.

In Chapter 5 of the *Bhagavad Gita*, Sri Krishna explains:

'I do nothing at all,' thinks the man who is in harmony, who realizes the truth. (v. 8)

Because in seeing, hearing, smelling, touching, in eating, walking, sleeping, breathing, in talking, grasping or relaxing, or even in opening or closing his eyes, he realizes, 'It is only the senses moving among the sense-objects.' (v. 9)

Then the next step is to 'give' the whole thing to the higher power. It can be the most difficult step, but paradoxically, if we have already successfully renounced any 'ownership' of the work, it is easy because we have nothing to give.

10. All our activities surrendered to the higher power
We are just the instrument of divine grace. As St Francis of Assisi said, "Not my will, O Lord, but thine." In that state of awareness there is no stress. If I am not the doer, and I am unattached to the outcome of the process, and anyway I realize it is 'all in good hands', how can I have a problem? So karma yoga, properly lived, is the ultimate anti-stress mechanism and takes us to partnership with the supreme consciousness. Through karma yoga, all life becomes a sacrament, as karma yoga and bhakti yoga become one at this high level.

14

The Path of Bhakti

Bhakti yoga – the path of devotion

Bhakti yoga is the path of devotion. The word *bhakti* comes from the root *bhaja*, which means to 'love, adore, be devoted, serve'. There is a great need for bhakti in most Western communities nowadays where so many of people's problems are caused by the 'spiritual vacuum' in their lives. We can relieve many of our problems, and evolve in all aspects of our being by finding our spiritual roots, whether we are basically of a devotional nature or not.

Bhakti is the means for coming closer to the essence of the highest consciousness, and eventually merging with it in oneness. Along the way the various stages of intensifying our closeness to the Lord (our personal object of devotion in the form of a spiritual master or a form of God) hold great benefits for the aspirant. People with a strongly activated anahata chakra in most aspects of their life are emotionalized. This can be a good thing if the quality of the emotion is positive, joy, love and compassion, etc., and the person has a suitable lifestyle outlet such as the helping, nurturing or religious professions. But many emotionalized anahata people can just as easily become embroiled in negative states such as jealousy, hate, resentment, dejection, depression, fear and emotional instability, and their life becomes a hell. Bhakti yoga – the concentrated pursuit of devotion, prayer, compassion and service for the benefit of others – is recommended to help transmute negative emotional states into positive feelings.

Fortunately, such people usually take happily and naturally to bhakti, and it allows them to express their emotional vitality through devotional channels. It is a very powerful way to evolve personality qualities of love and devotion, and as their emotions and feelings become more positive, it in turn transforms the quality of their devotion – another virtuous circle.

According to the *Srimad Bhagavatam* (as quoted by Swami Satyananda in *A Systematic Course in the Ancient Tantric Techniques of Yoga and Kriya*), there are nine methods that are recognized as the main ways to unfold bhakti in us.

1. Associating with wise and spiritual people, and hearing stories of the Lord's life, activities, virtues and powers.
2. Singing the glories of the Lord and dancing in ecstasy.
3. Continuous mindfulness of the divine. To some this may seem impractical because we have other things to do in our lives, but in full bhakti it is continuous at some level. Swami Niranjan gives the analogy of a mother's continuous awareness of her child. Many devotees of East and West use rosary beads to maintain the thread of awareness, and they also support their remembrance by keeping company with other devotees.
4. Service of the divine through serving humanity and the world. As Jesus said to the fourth wise man who helped other people: ". . . when I was hungry you gave me to eat, when I was thirsty you gave me to drink, when I was naked you clothed me, when I was homeless you took me in."
5. Worshipping the Lord through prayer, rituals and offerings from the heart, as is done in some homes, and all temples, churches, mosques, synagogues and other such places the world over.
6. Worshipping everyone and everything as being a form of the divine, and eventually realizing all as such. In the process one realizes one's own divine reality. At the same

time seeing everything as divine also eliminates our sense of duality, and bypasses the ego.

7. Loving the Lord through considering oneself as a servant of the divine, inculcating a sense of humility. Doing God's will merely as the vehicle for what is achieved through divine grace. This awareness of the hand of grace in everything strengthens one's faith more and more – an increasing virtuous circle.

8. Developing the feeling of being a close friend of the divine. The Lord becomes your innermost and dearest friend who will never desert you.

9. Total surrender – just being an instrument in the hands of the Lord. This leads to perfect union where lover, loving and the loved become one.

In *A Systematic Course in the Ancient Tantric Techniques of Yoga and Kriya,* Swami Satyananda describes the state of bhakti thus:

Bhakti is like making love to everything continuously, from humans, to the birds, the flowers . . . everything. You have no choice, for you realize their real nature and the nature of yourself and with this 'impossible' relationship, how is it possible not to feel love for everything? When you gain a peep, a glimpse of the essence of everything, the essence that is normally hidden from the eyes of most people, bhakti must result. Find out your real nature and the nature of everything and you will feel bhakti. You will never be the same person again. But this state comes only when one has the grace of expanded awareness. Once you have had a taste of the divine kiss from the lips of the beloved, then you will feel unquenchable thirst and aspiration for the supreme consciousness. The bhakta will chase and worship the supreme like a madman. One will forget everything except the divine. One divine kiss and one's whole life is transformed.

Most people don't attain this degree of bhakti; it is rare indeed. But as we tread the path of yoga, the love within us grows as we evolve the many aspects of our being, and this is helped if we follow the bhakti direction too. The whole thing expands much more if we are able to develop a relationship with a true spiritual master. The subtle relation he or she has with us must be experienced to be realized, and is enhanced if we have the opportunity to live with such a person in an ashram environment.

Many who don't have a very emotional nature will come into yoga with no intention of following the path of bhakti. Often the dynamic ones will pursue the physical practices of yoga and the path of karma yoga, perfecting their service to the world as a form of meditation in action, with minimum attachment to the benefits that result. Many often do this in an ashram environment. The psychic, more meditative people will be attracted to getting to know themselves by going within *(pratyahara)* and the meditation practices of raja yoga, and will pursue that direction. The intellectual people will be attracted to jnana yoga. They will dive into the philosophy of yoga and the understanding of the practices, trying to get more answers to 'why' – especially the 'why' about themselves. Next we will consider jnana yoga, the final path in our series, where all paths eventually meet.

15
Jnana Yoga in Our Life

The yoga of meditative awareness

The name comes from *jnana,* meaning knowledge, and *yoga,* meaning meditative awareness. So it is the yoga of 'wisdom' or 'knowledge', but not intellectual knowledge or reasoning. As the American comedian Woody Allen said: "Intellectuals can be absolutely brilliant, without having the faintest idea what's going on." Jnana yoga is an advanced spiritual practice *(sadhana),* a process of self-inquiry, with a strong concentrated mind.

In *Yoga Darshan* Swami Niranjan writes:

> The name itself creates some confusion because jnana literally means 'knowledge and wisdom', thus it is known as the yoga of knowledge and wisdom. The definition of yoga that we are using here is the process of meditative awareness. Therefore, in this context jnana yoga means the process of meditative awareness that brings us closer to our inner nature and gives birth to our intuitive faculties . . . It is a yoga of meditation in which the attitude is one of intense self-enquiry, where we become aware of our intuitive abilities and faculties.

So the knowledge we seek in jnana yoga isn't intellectual or rational knowledge as the name might suggest; it is wisdom, intuitive knowledge of our true nature, the process of meditative awareness that brings us closer to our inner nature. It is a process of enquiry that results in illumined or intuitive knowledge of this inner nature, and in expanded awareness – the 'big picture'.

Where do we start? Whereas the basis of bhakti yoga is belief, faith and devotion, on the path of jnana yoga we believe nothing.

Non-acceptance and non-belief

Yoga Darshan tells us:

> The starting point of jnana yoga is to believe nothing and accept nothing, because what we accept and believe is often erroneous and non-factual. Of course, we also have to use common sense. The concept of non-acceptance and non-belief is not to be taken in the context of our day-to-day life. There are certain things about which you have to use your own judgement and common sense, realizing fully that other people have experienced it, that there is a scientific basis for it, although you may not have had personal experience of it yourself. (The non-acceptance of jnana yoga) relates to the area or dimension where concepts become abstract, unclear and speculative, and have to be investigated. That is the aim of jnana yoga.

Self-analysis

The next stage of jnana yoga is self-analysis. Swami Niranjan continues in *Yoga Darshan*:

> This form of self-analysis is not abstract or abstruse; it is very definite. In fact, the practices of pratyahara and dharana may be classified as part of jnana yoga as well as raja yoga because through these practices we analyse ourselves. What is happening at the level of our thoughts? How are we being swayed by the thoughts, emotions and feelings? Do we have the ability to stop

them or to recall them at will? This kind of physical, mental, emotional and intellectual self-analysis is part of the techniques of jnana yoga. Something that gives us knowledge about ourselves is important because unless we understand the basic principles of our personality, we cannot progress on the path of jnana yoga.

Starting with the basic structure of jnana yoga, first the awareness of our needs has to be considered. What are the requirements of my body, mind and emotions? What are my social and family requirements? We need to have a clear-cut concept of these requirements. That becomes our personality, what we really need, apart from the ambitions. Then we need to observe and analyse what strengths and qualities we have and how they can help us to achieve our needs. This down-to-earth understanding of *our personality* will clear the dissipation of mind that is due to the influx of thousands and thousands of other ideas that are irrelevantly connected with our lives.

This practical approach of Swami Niranjan to the subject of jnana yoga is refreshing. So often we are advised to start our journey with questions such as "Who am I?" with the purpose of trying to personally identify with the atman (our spiritual reality). We may be asked to repeatedly think: "I am not this, or not that", to disidentify with everything that is not atman, or prepare to 'leap into the unknown'. Swami Niranjan says that these forms of awareness are among the last stages of jnana, and that the vast majority of us are nowhere near that. We have to start where we are, with simple self-analysis. For instance, we should be asking "why?" at the simplest levels of distress. Consider the following example:
1. You are experiencing stress and you realize it.
2. Your 'buttons' have been pushed – what are they?
3. Which klesha i.e. which of your desires has been thwarted?
4. Which chakra quality or area of your personality has been rattled – security, pleasure, power, self-esteem, desire for love, social desire?

5. What happened in the past to make you vulnerable in this way? One way to find out is to get into meditation and ask! Just that. When you are 'inside', ask the mind and often the answer will come up out of the unconscious and appear on your inner screen.

6. Use the insight to analyse how that experience has, in the past, affected your strengths, weaknesses, ambitions and needs, and how these can now be modified in the light of your new realization about yourself.

SWAN principle

Swami Niranjan has said that we have to analyse these Strengths, Weaknesses, Ambitions and Needs. This he calls the SWAN principle, from the initials of the four qualities. Our strengths are those qualities we have that contribute to the advancement of our spiritual evolution. The qualities that make us, for instance, more loving, more joyous, more confident with positive self-esteem, more basically secure, more able to communicate on a meaningful and intimate level with the people around us, more able to realize our psychic abilities and more aware of our own higher nature. We need to become aware of those qualities and develop them. Our weaknesses are those traits and tendencies that hold us back from advancing in those directions. As we become aware of them, we can curb their activities.

We have to learn to differentiate between our real *needs* and our *ambitions*. Ambitions are what we *desire* in life. They may motivate our actions to such an extent that they dominate our lives. They can be powerful because they are driven especially by our basic instincts of self-preservation and sex, though they may result from the desires of any of the qualities associated with the chakra systems. The strength of our ambitions or desires will be determined by how much we are identified with them. One way of simplifying our lives so that we may evolve is to clearly identify what our ambitions are, and not get them confused with our needs.

206

We have *needs* simply because we are occupying a body/ mind. They are the need for food, drink, oxygen, shelter, activity, rest, etc. In the larger context, needs comprise the physical, mental, emotional, intellectual, social and spiritual aspects of the person, as do other aspects of SWAN.

The American psychologist Abraham Maslow (1908–70), after studying a group of successful people he referred to as self-actualizers, came to the conclusion that we have an innate motivation to achieve our fullest potential by using our strengths. He called this potential *self-actualization*, and proposed that there is a *hierarchy of needs,* ascending from the basic needs of the body to more complex needs, culminating in self-actualization. We discussed this when dealing with the koshas. The needs he proposed (going from the most basic to the highest) are:

1. *Physiological needs* – food, drink, oxygen, shelter, activity, rest, etc.
2. *Safety needs* – protection from potentially dangerous situations.
3. *Belongingness and love needs* – acceptance and belonging to a group, receiving and giving love and affection.
4. *Esteem needs* – the esteem and respect of others, self-esteem and a sense of competence.
5. *Cognitive needs* – to know, to understand, to explore, and the need for meaning in life.
6. *Aesthetic needs* – beauty, balance, order and symmetry in our life.
7. *Self-actualization needs* – the urge to find self-fulfilment and to realize our full potential.

Maslow said that the lower needs have to be satisfied before the person is interested in higher needs. However, when they are predominantly satisfied, the person has an inner drive to develop through the higher stages. The yogis would agree with this, and see that inner drive as the 'call' of the atman – the spiritual spark that is the real Self, and which we are all striving to realize because it is inexorably pulling 'us' towards it.

Maslow went on to speak of *peak experiences*, which self-actualizers attain. He described them as "transient moments of self-actualization", which can vary from seeing nature in a new way, a deep intimacy, or a new smoothness and effortlessness in action.

It is interesting that Maslow saw all the stages of the hierarchy as 'needs', and didn't see the upper ones as just 'nice to have'. This agrees completely with the teachings of yoga, which tell us that the 'pull' of our highest individual consciousness – the atman – is irresistible, no matter at what stage of development we are. It is easy to see how, as we continue to evolve, we develop an increasing realization of that higher consciousness.

Non-attachment and right-understanding

To excel in jnana yoga one also needs the following abilities:

1. **Non-attachment** *(vairagya)* is dispassion, detachment from and non-entanglement in the objects of the world. It is akin to non-addiction to those things, which may include money, physical possessions, people in our lives, and more subtle influences such as reputation, admiration, social position, opinions, behaviour patterns, etc. It is freedom from *raga* (attraction) and *dwesha* (repulsion). Vairagya is also dispassion, disinterest and non-attachment to the fruits and benefits of one's activities. As we know, it is a fundamental requirement on the path of karma yoga.

2. **Right understanding** *(viveka)* is the ability to distinguish between the permanent and the changing. The person with advanced viveka constantly sees the world as a changing play, which is never confused with the permanence of the ultimate. At sattwic levels it is the positive ability to discriminate between real and unreal, eternal and decaying. Sometimes 'viveka' is defined as 'discrimination', but it is better to use 'right understanding' because discrimination is affected by the level of our evolvement, and can be a negative quality.

Viveka could be said to mean 'common sense', knowing how to act in the right way with the resources available. As the Serenity Prayer says: "Lord, grant me the serenity to accept the things I cannot change, the courage to change the things I can and the wisdom to know the difference." Viveka is that wisdom.

Vairagya and viveka are both faculties of *buddhi*, the higher mind. We can develop them by expanding our awareness to cover a wider area/field of consciousness. This is *meditative awareness,* awareness of every action at every moment. We aim at this in karma yoga, and indeed in every yoga practice. It is the attitude of the witness *(drashta)*, and needs effortless distinction between the doer and the witness. Without meditative awareness, meditation techniques cannot take us far. Vairagya and viveka go hand in hand – one leads to the other. We live in the present with spontaneity and naturalness, letting go of likes, dislikes, ego, and self-image, and developing simplicity.

Awakening of intuition

Yoga Darshan then deals with the next stage of jnana yoga:

In the intermediate stage of jnana yoga there are flashes of intuition. Such flashes can be experienced in the scientific world, in artistic creation, in musical composition. This happened to Einstein, Leonardo da Vinci, Michelangelo and Beethoven. How did it happen? When there is an obsession in the mind about something, and there is total concentration at that point, then the deeper forces of our personality come into play.

If you are really worried or tense about something which has stirred your mind, you are aware of the problem or fault with full intensity. The dissipated nature of mind which you had previously does not exist then. In that full intensity of mind, the deeper forces of your personality manifest. That full intensity of mind becomes an obsession. The positive experience of that obsession is indicated in the lives of people such as Einstein. However, that same obsession, when experienced with our distracted state of mind, becomes a great tension.

Although Einstein, da Vinci or Michelangelo did not know about jnana yoga, nowadays we can classify them as jnana yogis. They went beyond the existing limitations of predefined and preconceived knowledge and ideas, grabbed something and brought it back. Einstein went beyond the area of preconceived and accumulated knowledge. He picked up something from his intuitive dimension, brought it back and spent his lifetime rationalizing it. It is very difficult to spend one's life rationalizing an intuitive insight, but these flashes exist.

The mind is like a radio that is being tuned. In the process of being tuned it suddenly picks up a station that is broadcasting in a funny language, and we start thinking about it. What was that I heard? Usually we are not able to pick up the same station again because the radio waves become too weak or the transmission stops and we do not know when the next transmission will be; anything can happen. It is that tuning in to subtle frequencies which is the intermediate aspect of jnana yoga.

Advanced jnana yoga

What about the advanced stage of jnana yoga? Let's leave it for now. We can't understand such experiences in words, and besides, we don't have the time to prattle on about it; we are too busy working out our ordinary everyday conflicts. However, if you go back to Chapter 8 and read the parts on the stages of evolvement of the qualities of ajna chakra, you will get some idea of the progression of jnana yoga.

We can help the process of our jnana yoga to progress. There are a number of ways recommended for aspiring jnanis such as:

- Associating with wise people, being with people who are also on the yoga path, especially those pursuing jnana yoga.
- Reading and hearing words of wisdom, including those from knowledgeable and spiritual texts and scriptures, and relating them to your own experience.
- Contemplating any question with one-pointed awareness, maintaining total absorption on the point of one's inquiry.
- Believe nothing, only trust personal experience.
- Especially don't accept any ideologies. These include conceptual systems about human life or culture (yes, that includes yoga philosophy), required group thinking, social enculturation, and socio-political theories, assertions or aims.
- Don't accept any assumptions about the deeper questions of life, only be guided by experience.
- Don't identify with any roles, profession, titles, etc. – anything that will label you and fix you to a limited viewpoint of yourself or others. In other words, don't let anyone categorize you and don't do it to yourself.
- Combine other forms of yoga with your jnana yoga. This really means maintaining the jnana mind-state while practising other yogas. Maybe karma yoga and the meditation group are the most appropriate practices here, but the jnana yogi will maintain the jnani mind with the others too.

The big picture

Looking at the above list may start some people wondering if this path of jnana is such a good thing. The requirements seem to run counter to some of the things that people value most in life. Many love to follow established belief systems that seem to give them the answers to life; they love to be part of a community of fellow believers, whether religious, professional, social, political or other. Most people identify strongly with their professions and roles in life, especially if

211

those are viewed favourably by the rest of the community. Some actually 'become' their titles, such as Doctor, Professor, Reverend, Swami, etc., and they will grip tenaciously on to them as if their life depended on it – which in some respects it does. The path of jnana is not for them, but as we know, yoga is a treasure house of philosophy and practices that are available to all.

The person for whom jnana is natural has been a natural potential jnani all their life. They have always been asking "Why?" "Why not?" "How?" "How do you know?" and other such questions. They have always been sceptical, and when in a more tamasic frame of mind, maybe even cynical about what they see around them. Evolving their natural mind-set into jnana yoga just means that they incorporate the meditative awareness that is the crux of yoga and, if required, other aspects such as karma yoga, which offers a context of selfless service in which to expand the jnana.

This has been an overview of the lifestyle practices of yoga – the styles by which we can live our lives to enable us to evolve the aspects of our nature. In the next section we will explore the principles and practices of some of the yoga techniques we perform to augment that process of evolvement.

Yoga Techniques
for Evolvement

16

Physical Techniques

When we consider how we can use yoga practices to evolve the personality, we generally think of the techniques we are about to introduce here. However, the whole yogic lifestyle is included in the idea of 'yoga practices', so we have *'lifestyle practices'* and *'performed practices'* as a very balanced and rounded way of life. The lifestyle practices were discussed at length in the previous section. Now we should look at some of the performed practices: the physical techniques in this chapter and the meditation group in the next. But there are a few points we must consider.

Apart from some of the simple mental relaxation practices, yoga can NOT be learnt from a book, or sound cassettes or discs, or video cassettes or discs, or the internet or any other non-human source. We must learn from an experienced, qualified yoga teacher.

Let me tell you a personal tale. Back in about 1970, some time after my wife and I had met Swami Satyananda, and we had obtained a copy of his yoga instruction manual *Asana Pranayama Mudra Bandha (APMB)*, I decided to learn the Salute to the Sun (Surya Namaskara) series of postures. I wanted to impress my wife, who was already an experienced yoga teacher. I carefully read the instructions, looked at the pictures and practised the postures. When I had it 'perfect', I demonstrated it for my wife. She said, "That's lovely, darling. What is it?" I said, "What do you mean 'what is it', it is surya namaskara." "Not really," she said. I was doing every posture wrongly! And I was good at reading books. The problem was that the book could not tell me what I was doing wrong. It can't tell you either.

Books, etc., are good for reminding you after you have learnt from an expert. Bearing this in mind, the references to techniques in this book will be only brief, and are not meant to be instructions for the reader. Some people may record and listen to some of the 'closed eye' practices like Yoga Nidra, but that is not recommended either. It is better for a live teacher to guide you as to which of the techniques are best for you. It is important to observe this rule; for instance, people who have schizophrenia or borderline personality problems are best to avoid all of the closed-eye practices such as the meditation group – they do best with karma yoga, the postures and other 'externalizing' practices.

POSTURES (ASANAS)

Asanas are the postures that are usually associated with the name 'yoga'. They vary in complexity from simple stretching practices through to difficult advanced postures. It should be noted, however, that even the simplest asanas can have a profoundly beneficial effect on all dimensions of the person, especially the body/mind connection.

Swami Satyananda states in *APMB*:

The mind and body are not separate entities, although there is a tendency to think and act as if they are. The gross form of the mind is the body, and the subtle form of the body is the mind. The practice of asana integrates and harmonizes the two.

Both the body and the mind harbour knots. Every mental knot has a corresponding physical muscular knot and vice versa. The aim of asanas is to release these knots. Asanas release mental tensions by dealing with them on the physical level, acting somato-psychically, through

216

the body to the mind. For example, emotional tensions and suppression can tighten up and block the smooth functioning of the lungs, diaphragm and breathing process, contributing to a very debilitating form of illness in the form of asthma.

Muscular knots can occur anywhere in the body: tightness of the neck leading to cervical spondylosis, or of the face as neuralgia, etc. A well chosen set of asanas, combined with pranayama, shatkarmas, meditation and yoga nidra, is most effective in eliminating these knots, tackling them from both the physical and mental levels. The result is the release of dormant energy; the body becomes full of vitality and strength, the mind becomes light, creative, joyful and balanced.

Regular practice of asanas maintains the physical body in an optimum condition and promotes health, even in an unhealthy body. Through asana practice, the dormant potential energy is released and experienced as increased confidence in all areas of life.

Benefits
Some of the benefits we will receive from the postures in the process of evolving our personality are as follows.

Stretch: They stop the 'tension feedback'; the process whereby tension in the mind produces tension in the muscles of the body, which then creates more tension in the mind – another vicious circle. Asanas reverse this and substitute a virtuous circle instead.

Posture: They break the vicious circle created by mental and emotional tensions which produce abnormal posture (e.g. depressed posture, frightened posture, angry posture, etc.), which then exacerbates the mental and emotional problem. Straightening and relaxing in the new posture has a virtuous circle effect.

Relax: Asanas develop physical relaxation, which then relaxes the mind.

Vitality: They raise physical and mental energy by their physical action, and at the same time unblock energy that has been 'caught up' in tense muscles and joints.

Balance: Because of their equal 'feed in' from both sides, they help to balance the two hemispheres of the brain – ida and pingala.

Endorphins: Postures probably have a general balancing effect on the hormones and peptides of the body; they certainly do increase endorphins, the 'feel good' peptides.

Eighty-four of the most useful asanas are discussed in detail in *APMB*, too many to deal with here. The book also contains an index of illnesses and the asanas and other yogic practices used to treat them. It is valuable reading for any aspirant or therapist. Remember that we can learn the practices only from a qualified yoga instructor.

The asanas have many benefits. The introductory stretching postures taught to beginners in Satyananda Yoga develop the flexibility to do the more advanced postures correctly later. We will deal with those now and follow them with three standing postures. Then we will look at a more advanced but still introductory level group – the salute to the sun series.

FLEXIBILITY PRACTICES (PAWANMUKTASANA 1)

While performing these we concentrate completely, either on the positions themselves or on the breathing. Avoid any strain. After each two or three, we rest for a minute or so, remaining aware of the flow of the breath.

Base position (*Prarambhik Sthiti*)

All the flexibility practices are performed while sitting on the floor in the base position. We sit with the legs outstretched, with the palms of the hands on the floor to the sides and just behind the buttocks, with the head, neck and back straight, and the elbows straight. We lean back slightly, taking the support of the arms, with the eyes closed and the body relaxed. For maximum benefit we keep the eyes closed.

The body remains relaxed and we use only those muscles associated with the posture we are doing. We give our full awareness; we do not practise mechanically. We remain aware throughout the practice.

Toe bending (*Padanguli Naman*)

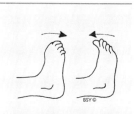

We sit in the base position, aware of the toes, and move the toes of both feet slowly backward and forward, keeping the feet upright and the ankles relaxed and motionless. We hold each position for a few seconds. Repeat 10 times, inhaling as the toes move backward, exhaling as the toes move forward.

Ankle bending (*Goolf Naman*)

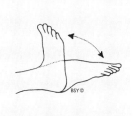

Remaining in the base position, with the feet slightly apart, we slowly move both feet backward and forward, bending them from the ankle joints. We try to stretch the feet forward to touch the floor and then draw them back towards the knees, as far as possible. We hold each position for a few seconds. Repeat 10 times, inhaling as the feet move backward, exhaling as the feet move forward.

219

Ankle rotation (*Goolf Chakra*)

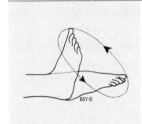

We remain in the base position, with the legs straight and separated a little, heels on the ground throughout the practice.

Stage 1: We slowly rotate the right foot clockwise from the ankle 10 times and then repeat 10 times anti-clockwise. Then repeat the same procedure with the left foot.

Stage 2: With the feet together, we slowly rotate both feet together in the same direction, keeping them in contact with each other. The knees are kept perfectly still. Do 10 times clockwise and then 10 times anti-clockwise.

Stage 3: With the feet separated, we slowly rotate both feet from the ankles together but in opposite directions. The big toes should touch each other on the inward stroke of each foot. Do 10 rotations in one direction and then 10 rotations in the opposite direction.

Inhale on the upward movement, exhale on the downward movement.

Ankle crank (*Goolf Ghoornan*)

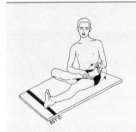

Remaining in the base position, we bend the right knee and bring the foot towards the buttock, then turn the knee out to the side and place the foot on the left thigh. Making sure the ankle is far enough over the thigh to be free for rotation, we hold the right ankle with the right hand to support the ankle and hold the toes of the right foot with the left hand. With the aid of the left hand, we slowly rotate the right foot 10 times clockwise, then 10 times anti-clockwise, inhaling on the upward movement and exhaling on the downward movement. Repeat with the left foot placed on the right thigh.

Kneecap contraction (*Janufalak Akarshan*)

Staying in the base position, we contract the front muscles of the right thigh, drawing the kneecap back towards the thigh, holding the contraction for 5 seconds, counting mentally. Then we release the contraction and let the kneecap return to its normal position. We practise this 5 times, inhaling while contracting, holding the breath during the contraction, and exhaling while relaxing the knee muscles. Repeat with the left kneecap 5 times, then with both kneecaps together.

Knee bending (*Janu Naman*)

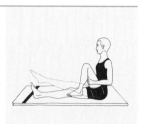

Staying in the base position, keeping the head and spine straight, we bend the right knee and clasp the hands under the right thigh. Then we straighten the right leg with full contraction of the front thigh muscles, keeping the hands under the thigh but straightening the arms. The heel or toes should not touch the floor. Then we bend the right leg at the knee so that the thigh comes up close to the chest and the heel near the buttock. We inhale while straightening the leg, then exhale while bending the leg. Practise 10 rounds with the right leg and then 10 rounds with the left leg.

Knee crank (*Janu Chakra*)

Sitting in the base position, we bend the right leg at the knee, and place the hands under the right thigh, interlocking the fingers, or crossing the arms and holding the elbows. Then we rotate the lower leg from the knee in a large circular movement, trying to straighten the leg at the top of the upward movement. The upper leg and trunk should be completely still. We rotate 10 times clockwise and then 10 times anti-clockwise, and then repeat with the left leg, inhaling on the upward movement, and exhaling on the downward movement.

Half butterfly (*Ardha Titali Asana*)

Sitting in the base position, we bend the right leg and place the right foot as far up on the left thigh as possible. Place the right hand on top of the bent right knee, and hold the right foot with the left hand. While breathing in, we gently move the right knee up towards the chest, and then while breathing out, we gently push the knee down and try to touch the knee to the floor. This movement should not be forced in any way. The trunk should not move and the leg muscles should be passive, the movement being achieved by the exertion of the right arm. We slowly practise 10 up and down movements, and then practise on the other side.

Hip rotation (*Shroni Chakra*)

Sitting in the base position, we bend the right leg and place the right foot as far up on the left thigh as possible, without straining. Place the right hand on top of the bent right knee, and hold the right foot with the left hand. Then using the muscles of the right arm, rotate the right knee in a circle trying to make the circular movement as large as possible. We practise 10 rotations clockwise and then 10 rotations anti-clockwise, inhaling on the upward movement and exhaling on the downward movement, then straighten the leg slowly. We release the knee and repeat with the left leg.

Full butterfly (*Poorna Titali Asana*)

We sit in the base position, bend the knees and bring the soles of the feet together, keeping the heels as close to the body as possible, fully relaxing the inner thigh muscles.

Stage 1: We clasp the feet with both hands, and gently move the knees up and down, using the elbows as levers to press the legs down. We try to touch the knees to the ground on the downward stroke, but do not use any force. Practise 30 to 50 up and down movements.

Stage 2: Keeping the soles of the feet together, we place the hands on the knees, and using the palms, gently push the knees down towards the floor, allowing them to spring up again. No force should be used for this movement. We repeat 20 to 30 times, then straighten the legs and relax.

Breathing is normal, unrelated to the practice.

Hand clenching (*Mushtika Bandhana*)

We sit in the base position or a cross-legged pose and hold both arms straight in front of the body at shoulder level. We alternately open the hands, palms down, and stretch the fingers as wide apart as possible, then close the fingers to make a tight fist with the thumb inside. Repeat 10 times. Inhale while opening the hands and exhale while closing the hands, then rest.

Wrist bending (*Manibandha Naman*)

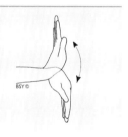

Remaining in the base position or a cross-legged pose, we again stretch the arms in front of the body at shoulder level, palms facing the floor. Keeping the palms open and fingers straight throughout the entire practice, we bend the hands backward from the wrists with the fingers pointing toward the ceiling, then bend the hands forward from the wrists so that the fingers point toward the floor. Elbows, knuckle joints and fingers are kept straight throughout the practice. We repeat 10 times, inhaling with the backward movement and exhaling with the forward movement.

Wrist joint rotation (*Manibandha Chakra*)

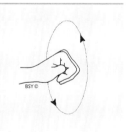

Remain in the base position or a comfortable cross-legged pose, and keep the back straight.

Stage 1: We extend the right arm forward at shoulder level and make a fist with the right hand, with the thumb inside – the left hand may be used as a support if necessary. This is the starting position. We then slowly rotate the fist about the wrist, and make as large a circle as possible, ensuring that the forearm remains perfectly straight and still. We practise 10 times clockwise and 10 times anti-clockwise, then repeat the same with the left fist.

Stage 2: We extend both arms in front of the body with the fists clenched, keeping the arms straight and at shoulder level, then rotate the fists together in the same direction, 10 times in each direction.

Stage 3: Practise as in stage 2, but rotate the fists together in opposite directions, again 10 times each way.

Elbow bending (*Kehuni Naman*)

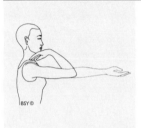

Remain in the base position or a cross-legged pose.

Stage 1: We stretch the arms in front of the body at shoulder level, with the hands open and the palms facing up. We bend the arms at the elbows and touch the fingers to the shoulders, then completely straighten the arms again. We repeat this 10 times, inhaling while straightening the arms and exhaling while bending the arms.

Stage 2: Extending the arms sideways at shoulder level, hands open and palms facing the ceiling, we bend the arms at the elbows and touch the fingers to the shoulders, then again straighten the arms sideways. We repeat this 10 times, inhaling while straightening the arms and exhaling while bending the arms.

Shoulder socket rotation (*Skandha Chakra*)

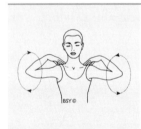

We place the fingers of the left hand on the left shoulder and the fingers of the right hand on the right shoulder. Then we fully rotate both elbows at the same time in a large circle, trying to touch the elbows in front of the chest on the forward movement. We try to touch the ears while moving up, stretch the arms back in the backward movement, and touch the sides of the trunk while coming down. We do this slowly 10 times coming up in the front, and then 10 times going down in front, inhaling on the upward movement, and exhaling on the downward movement in each case.

Neck movements (*Greeva Sanchalana*)

We sit in the base position or a cross-legged pose with the hands resting on the knees.

Stage 1: We close the eyes and slowly move the head forward, trying to touch the chin to the chest, then move the head as far back as is comfortable, without strain. We feel the stretch of the muscles in the front and back of the neck. We do this 10 times, inhaling on the backward movement and exhaling on the forward movement.

Stage 2: Remaining in the same position, we face directly forward, keeping the eyes closed and shoulders relaxed. We slowly tilt the head over to the right so that the right ear comes towards the right shoulder, without turning the head or raising the shoulders. Then tilt the head to the left side so that the left ear comes towards the left shoulder. We practise 10 rounds, inhaling on the upward movement and exhaling on the downward movement. Do not strain during this practice.

Stage 3: Remaining in the base position, and keeping the head upright and the eyes closed, we gently turn the head to the right so that the chin is in line with the shoulder, feeling the release of tension in the neck muscles and the loosening of the neck joints. Then slowly turn the head to the left as far as is comfortable. Without strain, we practise 10 times on each side, inhaling while turning to the front, and exhaling while turning to the side.

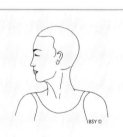

Stage 4: Remaining in the same position with the eyes closed, we slowly rotate the head downward, to the right, backward and then to the left side in a relaxed, smooth, rhythmic, circular movement, inhaling as the head moves up, and exhaling as the head moves down. We can feel the shifting stretch around the neck and the loosening up of the joints and muscles of the neck. We practise 10 times clockwise

and then 10 times anti-clockwise, making sure not to strain. After the practice, we keep the neck straight and the eyes closed, remaining aware of the sensations in the head and neck. If dizziness occurs, we open the eyes.

Contra-indications: These four neck movements should not be performed by elderly people and those suffering from low blood pressure, very high blood pressure or extreme cervical spondylosis. The advice of an expert should be sought for any of these problems. Patients of cervical spondylosis should strictly avoid forward bending of the neck or any painful movements.

STANDING POSTURES

These three standing postures are excellent for limbering the spine. They are easy to do and supplement the flexibility practices, which don't have asanas for the main part of the spine. They are also three of the five postures we use for the intestinal wash (more later).

Palm tree pose (*Tadasana*)

We stand with the feet together or about 10 cm apart, and the arms by the sides, steady the body and distribute the weight equally on both feet. Then we interlock the fingers, turn the palms upward and place the backs of the hands on top of the head. We fix the eyes at a point on the wall slightly above the level of the head (the eyes remain fixed on this point throughout the practice). Inhale and stretch the arms, shoulders and chest upward, raising the heels, coming up onto the toes and stretching the whole body from top to bottom, without losing balance or moving the feet.

We hold the breath and the position for a few seconds, then lower the heels while breathing out and returning the hands to the top of the head. Relax for a few seconds before performing the next round. We do 5 to 10 rounds.

Although at first some people find it difficult to maintain balance, it becomes easier with practice.

226

Swaying palm tree pose (*Tiryaka Tadasana*)

We stand with the feet about half a metre apart, fix the gaze on a point directly in front, interlock the fingers and turn the palms outward. We inhale and raise the arms over the head, then while exhaling, bend to the left side from the waist, making sure we don't bend forward or backward or twist the trunk. We hold the position for a few seconds while retaining the breath outside, then inhale and slowly come to the upright position.

Then we repeat it on the right side, hold for a few seconds, come up to the upright position, and exhale while bringing the arms down to the sides. We do 5 to 10 rounds.

Waist rotating pose (*Kati Chakrasana*)

For this asana we stand with the feet about half a metre apart, the arms by the sides, and take a deep breath in while raising the straight arms to shoulder level. As we breathe *out* and twist the body to the left, we bring the right hand to the left shoulder and wrap the left arm around the back, bringing the left hand around the right side of the waist. Then we look over the left shoulder as far as possible, keeping the back of the neck straight and imagining that the top of the spine is the fixed point around which the head turns.

We hold the breath for two seconds, accentuate the twist and try to gently stretch the abdomen. Then as we inhale, we return to the starting position. Repeat on the other side to complete one round. The feet are kept firmly on the ground while twisting, and the arms and back are relaxed as much as possible throughout the practice.

We practise 5 to 10 rounds, ensuring that the rotation is done smoothly and the rest of the movements are relaxed and spontaneous.

SALUTE TO THE SUN (SURYA NAMASKARA)

This series is considered a complete spiritual practice in itself because it can include asanas, pranayamas, mantras and meditation techniques. It is said to have a direct vitalizing effect on the solar energy of the body which flows through pingala nadi. Regular practice regulates pingala nadi, whether it is underactive or overactive. Regulation of pingala nadi leads to a balanced energy system at both the mental and physical levels. It also activates all of the chakra systems, so it is a well balanced series of postures. Even though it is included in the beginners' level group, most people will need to limber up with the flexibility practices for some months first, so that they can get into the positions correctly. It is an excellent group with which to start morning practice.

Position 1: Prayer pose (*Pranamasana*)

We stand upright with the feet together, the eyes closed, and the whole body relaxed. Then slowly bend the elbows and place the palms together in front of the chest in namaskara mudra, mentally offering homage to the sun, the source of all life.

Breathing is normal. Concentration is on anahata chakra.

Position 2: Raised arms pose (*Hasta Utthanasana*)

We raise and stretch both arms above the head, keeping the arms a shoulder width apart, then gently tilt the head, arms and upper trunk backward.

Inhale while raising the arms. Concentration is on vishuddhi chakra.

228

Position 3: Hand to foot pose (*Padahastasana*)

We bend forward, but without straining, until the fingers or palms of the hands touch the floor on either side of the feet (or as near as possible), and try to touch the knees with the forehead, keeping the knees straight.

Exhale while bending forward. Concentration is on swadhisthana chakra.

Position 4: Equestrian pose (*Ashwa Sanchalanasana*)

We place the palms of the hands flat on the floor beside the feet (you may bend the knees if necessary). Stretch the right leg back as far as possible, at the same time bending the left knee, keeping the left foot on the floor in the same position; the arms remain straight.

In the final position, the weight of the body is supported on both hands, the left foot, right knee and the toes of the right foot. The head should be tilted backward, the back arched and the inner gaze directed upward to the eyebrow centre.

Inhale while stretching the right leg back. Concentration is on ajna chakra.

Position 5: Mountain pose (*Parvatasana*)

Then we take the left foot back beside the right foot, simultaneously raising the buttocks and lowering the head between the arms, so that the back and legs form two sides of a triangle, with the legs and arms straight in the final position.

We try to keep the heels on the floor in the final pose and bring the head towards the knees, but without straining.

229

Exhale while taking the left leg back. Concentration is on vishuddhi chakra.

Position 6: Salute with eight points (*Ashtanga Namaskara*)

We lower the knees, chest and chin to the floor, so that in the final position only the toes, knees, chest, hands and chin touch the floor (eight points of the body), with the buttocks, hips and abdomen raised. The knees, chest and chin should touch the floor simultaneously, but if this is not possible, we first lower the knees, then the chest, and finally the chin.

The breath is held outside in this pose. Concentration is on manipura chakra.

Position 7: Cobra pose (*Bhujangasana*)

Next we lower the buttocks and hips to the floor, straightening the elbows, arching the back and pushing the chest forward into the cobra pose, and bending the head back, with the gaze directed upward to the eyebrow centre.

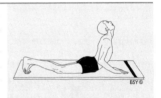

The thighs and hips remain on the floor and the arms support the trunk, but unless the spine is very flexible the arms remain slightly bent.

Inhale while raising the torso and arching the back. Concentration is on swadhisthana chakra.

Position 8: Mountain pose (*Parvatasana*)

This stage is a repeat of position 5. From the cobra, we assume the mountain pose (the hands and feet not moving from position 7), raising the buttocks and lowering the heels to the floor.

Exhale while raising the buttocks. Concentration is on vishuddhi chakra.

Position 9: Equestrian pose (*Ashwa Sanchalanasana*)

This stage is the same as position 4. Keeping the palms flat on the floor, we bend the left leg and bring the left foot forward between the hands, simultaneously lowering the right knee so that it touches the floor and pushing the pelvis forward. The head is tilted backward, the back arched, and gaze is at the eyebrow centre.

Inhale while assuming the pose. Concentration is on ajna chakra.

Position 10: Hand to foot pose (*Padahastasana*)

This position is a repeat of position 3. We bring the right foot forward next to the left foot, straighten both knees, and bring the forehead as close to the knees as possible without straining.

Exhale while performing the movement. Concentration is on swadhisthana chakra.

Position 11: Raised arms pose (*Hasta Utthanasana*)

This stage is a repeat of position 2. We raise the torso and stretch the arms above the head, keeping the arms separated a shoulder width apart, then bend the head, arms and upper trunk backward.

Inhale while straightening the body. Concentration is on vishuddhi chakra.

Position 12: Prayer pose (*Pranamasana*)

This is the final position and is the same as position 1. We bring the palms together in front of the chest.

Exhale while assuming the final position. Concentration is on anahata chakra.

Positions 13–24: The twelve positions of Salute to the Sun are practised twice to complete one round. Positions 1 to 12 constitute half a round. In the second half, the positions are repeated with two small changes to the equestrian pose as follows:

a) In position 16, instead of stretching the right foot backward, we stretch the left foot back.

b) In position 21, we bend the right leg and bring the right foot between the hands.

Conclusion: On the completion of each *half* round of Salute to the Sun, we lower the arms to the side, relax the body and concentrate on the breath until it returns to normal. After completing the series, we practise the corpse pose *(shavasana)* for some minutes, to allow the heartbeat and respiration to return to normal and all the muscles to relax.

Corpse Pose (*Shavasana*)

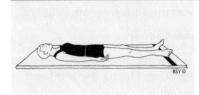

We lie flat on the back with the head and spine in a straight line, on a comfortable surface, with a thin pillow or folded cloth below the head if required to prevent discomfort. The arms are about 15 cm away from the body, palms facing upward, the fingers are curled up slightly, the feet are slightly apart in a comfortable position, and the eyes are closed.

We relax the whole body and stop all physical movement, and become aware of the flow of the natural breath, allowing it to become rhythmic and relaxed. Then we begin to count the breaths from number 27 backwards to zero, mentally repeating "breath is flowing in 27, breath is flowing out 27, breath is flowing in 26, breath is flowing out 26 . . . ", and so on, back to zero. If the mind wanders and the next number is forgotten, we bring it back to the counting and start again at 27. If we can keep the mind on the breath for a few minutes, the body usually relaxes. Concentration is on ajna chakra.

Note: The benefits, contra-indications and other details of the asanas can be read in the source book *Asana Pranayama Mudra Bandha (APMB)* by Swami Satyananda Saraswati.

CLEANSING PRACTICES (SHATKARMAS)

This is a series of six groups of cleansing practices that are recommended for people who have various illnesses, and also for aspirants who are beginning advanced practices. Done in the correct sequence, the shatkarmas are designed to clean and purify the gross body, then stimulate the pranic energy, then stop mental dissipation, and then concentrate the mind. After this preparation, the practices of meditation can progress smoothly.

The three mentioned here are especially relevant to our subject – the nasal cleansing practice, which balances the nostril flows and activates ajna, the regurgitative cleansing, which relieves tension build-up in the manipura region, and the intestinal wash, which, combined with the other two, activates all the chakras in a balanced way.

Nasal wash (*Jala Neti*)

Neti removes mucus and pollution from the nasal passages, and helps to prevent or manage conditions such as asthma, bronchitis, sinusitis, migraine and epilepsy. It stimulates the various nerve endings in the nose, improving the activities of the brain and the overall health of the individual. Over a period of months, if the nostrils are structurally normal, a balance is  brought about between the right and left nostrils and the corresponding left and right brain hemispheres, inducing a state of harmony and balance throughout. Most importantly, however, neti helps to awaken ajna chakra.

Stage 1: Washing the nostrils

A special neti pot or even a teapot can be used. We fill the neti pot with warm (body temperature) salty water (one teaspoonful of salt per half litre of water), stand squarely, legs apart, with the body weight evenly distributed between the feet, and lean forward, close the eyes for a minute or so and relax the whole body.

Then we tilt the head to one side and slightly back, begin to breathe through the mouth, and gently insert the nozzle into the uppermost nostril. There should be no force; the nozzle should press gently but firmly against the side of the nostril so that no water leakage occurs.

Then we tilt the neti pot in such a way that water runs into the nostril and not down the face, adjusting the body position to enable the water to pass out through the nostril on the other side.

When half the water has passed through the nostrils, we remove the nozzle from the nostril, centre the head and let the water run out of the nose, and remove any mucus from the nose by blowing gently.

Then we tilt the head to the opposite side and repeat the process, placing the nozzle of the pot in the other nostril. After completing this process, the nostrils are thoroughly dried in the following way.

Stage 2: Drying the nostrils

1. We stand erect, close the right nostril with the right thumb, and breathe in and out through the left nostril 5 to 10 times in quick succession, emphasizing the exhalation, then repeat through the right nostril, with the left nostril closed. We do this twice.

233

2. Then we bend forward from the waist so that the trunk is horizontal, and repeat the same process as described above, but this time tilting the head to the right, and closing the left nostril. We repeat this on the other side, tilting the head to the left and closing the right nostril. Finally, we repeat it again with the head centred, breathing through both nostrils.
3. Next we stand erect with the feet apart. Close the right nostril and exhale rapidly and forcefully, while bending forward from the waist. We then inhale normally while returning to the upright position. This is done 5 to 10 times, then repeated with the right nostril open, and then with both nostrils open.

Note: Neti is usually practised once daily after bathing, or as recommended by a yoga teacher or therapist. To relieve severe colds, chronic catarrh or other ailments, we may do it up to 3 times daily.

Regurgitative cleansing (*Kunjal Kriya*)

Preparation
This is a technique of washing out the stomach. We have to tickle the back of the tongue to regurgitate the water so we make sure the hands are washed and the nails are carefully trimmed and smoothed. Kunjal is an excellent practice for asthma, anxiety and tension, and it helps to release pent-up emotions and emotional blocks or feelings of 'heaviness in the heart' caused by inner and external conflict and pressures. The biggest obstacle is the mental block that people have towards the idea of vomiting.

We prepare about two litres of lukewarm (body temperature) water, adding one teaspoonful of salt per litre according to taste. Plain water may be used on the advice of a yoga teacher.

Technique
We stand near a sink or toilet, or if the weather is warm in a suitable place outside, and drink at least 6 glasses of the prepared water one after the other as quickly as possible, until it feels that the stomach cannot hold any more. It is most important to drink fast and not just sip the water.

When the stomach is full, the urge to vomit usually occurs automatically, so we lean forward, keeping the trunk as horizontal as possible, open the mouth, place the middle and index fingers of the right hand as far back on the tongue as possible, and gently rub and press the back of the tongue. This induces the water to gush out from the stomach.

If there is no expulsion of water, it means the tips of the fingers are not far enough down the throat or that the tongue is not being pressed. The more we relax into the practice, the easier it is.

During the expulsion of water, we may remove the fingers from the mouth, although this is not necessary. When the flow of water ceases, we again place the fingers in the mouth and repeat the process, and continue in this way until the stomach is empty.

Intestinal washing (*Shankhaprakshalana*)

This practice washes out the whole gastrointestinal tract with warm salty water. It is an excellent purification practice, and when followed by the nasal wash (neti) and regurgitative cleansing (kunjal), helps to awaken all of the chakra circuits.

How do we do it?

We drink two glasses of warm salty water as quickly as possible, then perform five asanas eight times each in the correct sequence (these include the three standing asanas we have already mentioned), opening the valves of the intestines. This is one complete round. Then we drink two more glasses of warm salty water and again repeat the five asanas eight times each, and repeat this process a third time.

After the third round, we go to the toilet and see if there is any movement in the bowels. If they have not yet started, we do not strain, but after a few minutes or so come out, regardless of whether there has been any movement or not.

Then we drink two more glasses, repeat the five asanas eight times, and again go to the toilet, but do not use force to produce a bowel movement. Then we continue drinking the water, performing the asanas and going to the toilet when the pressure builds up. We spend as little time in the toilet as possible, a minute or so is enough, because the aim is to build up the internal cleansing pressure.

At first, solid stool is evacuated, followed by a mixture of stool and water, then as the practice progresses more water and less solid stool are excreted. Eventually, cloudy yellow water and, finally, almost clear water are evacuated.

Sixteen glasses are generally required before perfectly clear water is evacuated, but it varies from person to person.

After resting for 10 minutes on completing the internal wash, we perform the regurgitative cleansing *(kunjal)*, followed by the nasal wash *(neti)*. Then we rest for exactly 45 minutes, after which we eat a large helping of a specially prepared food *(khichari)*. Then we rest (but not sleep) for another three hours. Six hours after the first special meal we have another meal of khichari. The stomach must be filled to capacity at both meals, even if there is no feeling of hunger. We have to observe strict food restrictions for at least one month after the practice.

Warning: This practice should only be attempted in an ashram or yoga centre under expert guidance.

Short intestinal wash *(Laghoo Shankhaprakshalana)*

This is the short practice, in which only 6 glasses of water are drunk. We practise it in the morning when the stomach is completely empty, before any food or drink is taken.

Two litres of warm salted water are prepared, then we quickly drink two glasses of the prepared water, and perform the five shankhaprakshalana asanas eight times. Then we drink two more glasses of water and repeat the asanas eight times each, then repeat the process for a third and last time. After that we go to the toilet but do not strain, whether there is a bowel movement or not.

If there is no motion immediately, it will come later on. Regurgitative cleansing *(kunjal)*, followed by the nasal wash *(neti)* may be performed immediately after completing the practice.

BREATH PRACTICES (PRANAYAMA)

The usual description of 'pranayama' is 'breath control', but this does not indicate the full meaning of the word. Pranayama is more than just a way of getting more oxygen into the body; it deals with the whole area of vitality and the pranamaya kosha. The different pranayama practices can also create relaxation of the body, mind and emotions, and a general balancing of the organism. We will look at six pranayamas here, and describe some of the benefits we can expect to gain from them.

Natural breathing

This simple technique introduces us to our own respiratory system and breathing patterns. It is very relaxing physically and mentally, and may be practised at any time. Awareness of the breathing process is itself sufficient to slow down the respiratory rate and establish a more relaxed rhythm.

Natural breathing technique

We sit in a comfortable position or lie in the corpse pose (*shavasana*) and relax the whole body. Then we simply observe the natural and spontaneous breathing process, develop total awareness of the rhythmic flow of the breath and feel the breath flowing in and out of the nose, without trying to control the breath in any way.

We notice that the breath is cool as it enters the nostrils and warm as it flows out, just observing this with the attitude of a detached witness.

Then after a short while we feel the breath flowing in and out at the back of the mouth above the throat.

Now we become aware of the region of the throat and feel the breath flowing in the throat.

Then we become aware of the region of the chest and feel the breath flowing in the trachea and bronchial tubes, then in the lungs, aware of the lungs expanding and relaxing. Then to the rib cage and observe the expansion and relaxation of this area.

Then we become aware of the abdomen, feeling the abdomen move upward on inhalation and downward on exhalation.

Finally, we become aware of the whole breathing process from the nostrils to the abdomen and continue observing it for some time.

Then after some time we bring the awareness back to observing the physical body as one unit, and open the eyes.

Yogic breathing

Yogic breathing combines abdominal breathing, chest breathing and high chest breathing. It is used to maximize inhalation and exhalation so we can gain control of the breath, correct poor breathing habits and increase oxygen intake. It is excellent for singers and musicians who use their breath.

It may be practised at any time and is especially useful in situations of high stress or anger, as it helps to calm the nerves. However, while its inclusion in a daily yoga program will correct and deepen natural breathing patterns, yogic breathing itself should not be performed continually.

Yogic breathing technique

We sit in a comfortable posture or lie in the corpse pose *(shavasana)* and keep the whole body relaxed throughout the practice.

First we inhale slowly and deeply, allowing the abdomen to expand fully, trying to breathe so slowly that little or no sound of the breath can be heard, and feeling the air reaching into the bottom of the lungs.

Then at the end of abdominal expansion we start to expand the chest outward and upward, until the ribs are fully expanded.

Then we inhale a little more, until expansion is felt in the upper portion of the lungs around the base of the neck. The shoulders and collar bone also move up slightly, and some tension will be felt in the neck muscles, as we feel the air filling the upper lobes of the lungs.

This completes one inhalation. The whole process is one continuous movement, each phase of breathing merging into the next without any obvious transition point, without any jerks or unnecessary strain – the breathing should be like the swell of the sea.

Then we start the exhalation by allowing the lower neck and upper chest to relax, then allowing the chest to contract downward and then inward, and then allowing the diaphragm to move upward and toward the chest.

Without straining, we try to empty the lungs as much as possible by drawing or pulling the abdominal wall as near as possible to the spine, allowing the entire movement to be harmonious and flowing. We hold the breath for a few seconds at the end of exhalation, then start the next inhalation.

Initially we perform 5 to 10 rounds and slowly increase to 10 minutes daily.

Yogic breathing is used in most pranayamas. The main requirement, however, is that respiration be comfortable and relaxed. Consequently, once awareness and control of the breathing process has been established, the inhalation into the upper section of the lungs is usually dropped, and the yogic breathing is modified to become a combination of abdominal and thoracic breathing. The breath should flow naturally and not be forced.

Psychic breath (*Ujjayi Pranayama*)

This practice is used in yoga therapy to soothe the nervous system and calm the mind. It has a profoundly relaxing effect at the psychic level, and as it helps to relieve insomnia, it may also be practised lying down just before sleep.

We sit in any comfortable position, with the eyes closed and the whole body relaxed, become aware of the breath in the nostrils, and allow the breathing to become calm and rhythmic.

After some time we become aware of the throat, and try to feel or to imagine that the breath is being drawn in and out through the throat and not through the nostrils; almost as if inhalation and exhalation are taking place just through the throat.

As the breathing becomes slower and deeper, we gently contract the glottis so that a soft snoring sound, like the breathing of a sleeping baby, is produced in the throat. Both inhalation and exhalation are long, deep and controlled. It is essentially yogic breathing while concentrating on the sound produced by the breath in the throat.

The sound of the breath should not be very loud. It should just be audible to the practitioner, but not to another person unless they are sitting very close.

Alternate nostril breathing (*Nadi Shodhana*)

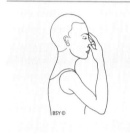

This technique induces tranquillity, clarity of thought and concentration, and is recommended for those engaged in mental work. But most importantly, it also balances the flow of the breath through the two nostrils, so it balances the activities of the two sides of the brain, causes sushumna nadi to flow and so readies one for meditation.

Hand position

We hold the fingers of the right hand in front of the face, resting the index and middle fingers gently on the point between the eyebrows, with both fingers relaxed. The thumb is then covering the right nostril and the ring finger is covering the left. During the practice, these two fingers are the ones that control the flow of breath in the nostrils by alternately pressing on one nostril, blocking the flow of breath, and then the other. The little finger is comfortably folded.

Technique

We sit in a comfortable meditation posture (those who cannot sit in a meditation posture may sit against a wall with the legs outstretched or in a chair which has a straight back), keeping the head and spine upright, the body relaxed and the eyes closed.

We practise yogic breathing for some time, then place the hand over the face as explained above, place the left hand on the knee, and close the right nostril with the thumb.

Then we inhale and exhale through the left nostril 5 times at a normal rate, being aware of each breath, making sure that there is no sound as the air passes through the nostrils. After 5 breaths we release the pressure of the thumb on the right nostril and press the left nostril with the ring finger, blocking the flow of air, and inhale and exhale through

239

the right nostril 5 times. Then we lower the hand and breathe 5 times through both nostrils together, and this completes one round.

It is usual to practise 5 rounds or for 3 to 5 minutes.

Frontal brain cleansing breath (*Kapalbhati Pranayama*)

This practice purifies ida and pingala nadis, and also removes distractions from the mind. It is used to energize the mind for mental work, to remove sleepiness and to prepare the mind for meditation.

We sit in a comfortable posture, with the head and spine straight and the hands resting on the knees, the eyes closed and the body relaxed.

We inhale deeply through both nostrils, expanding the abdomen, and then without straining, exhale with a forceful contraction of the abdominal muscles.

The next inhalation takes place by passively allowing the abdominal muscles to expand – inhalation being a spontaneous or passive recoil, involving no effort.

We perform 10 respirations to begin with, counting each respiration mentally, then after completing the 10 rapid breaths in succession, we inhale and exhale deeply to end one round. It is usual to practise 3 to 5 rounds.

After completing the practice, we maintain awareness of the void in the region of the eyebrow centre, feeling an all-pervading calmness and emptiness of the mind.

It is important that the rapid breathing used in these techniques be from the abdomen and not from the chest.

Humming bee breath (*Bhramari Pranayama*)

This practice is the great tranquillizer. It relieves stress and cerebral tension, alleviating anger, anxiety and insomnia, and reducing blood pressure. It also strengthens and improves the voice.

We sit in a comfortable posture, with the spinal cord and head straight, the hands resting on the knees, the eyes closed and the body relaxed.

The lips remain gently closed with the teeth slightly separated, and the tongue on the bottom of the mouth throughout the practice, which allows the sound vibration to be heard and felt more distinctly in the brain. The jaws are relaxed.

We then raise the arms sideways with the elbows bent, bringing the hands to the ears, using the index or middle finger to plug the ears. (The small flaps of the ears may be pressed without inserting the fingers.)

We become aware of the centre of the head, where ajna chakra is located, and keeping the body absolutely still, breathe in deeply through the nose, then exhale slowly and in a controlled manner while making a deep, steady *humming* sound like that of a bee. The humming sound is soft, mellow, smooth, even and continuous for the duration of the exhalation, making the centre of the head reverberate. This is one round, then at the end of exhalation, we breathe in deeply again and repeat the process. It is usual to perform 5 rounds before meditation, or for 5 or even 10 minutes for immediate relief of stress.

ATTITUDES AND LOCKS (MUDRAS AND BANDHAS)

These are postural attitudes and muscle locks that have various effects. We will mention just one of them.

Perineum contraction (*Moola Bandha*)

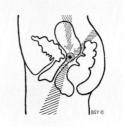

Emotional control: Once we know how to do this practice, it only needs to be done occasionally. It is introduced here because it is very good for stopping – virtually dissolving – emotional reactions such as anger, grief, anxiety, and even the positive ones. If we get into an emotional state and are about to act, all we need to do is contract moola bandha and the emotion will stop, giving us time to choose a better action.

Stage 1: We sit comfortably, close the eyes, relax the whole body, and maintain awareness of the natural breath for a short while. Then we focus the awareness on the region of the perineum, and contract this region by pulling up on the muscles of the pelvic floor (the muscles in women that tighten the vaginal entrance – men have them too) and then relaxing them. We continue to briefly contract and relax the perineal region as rhythmically and evenly as possible for about a minute.

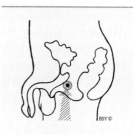

Stage 2: Now we slowly contract the perineal region and hold the contraction, continuing to breathe normally, while being totally aware

of the physical sensation. Then we contract a little tighter, but keep the rest of the body relaxed. We contract only those muscles related to the mooladhara region, right in the centre of the perineum.

In the beginning the anal and urinary sphincters also contract, but as we develop greater awareness and control, this is minimized and eventually ceases. Ultimately, we feel only the one point contracting. We repeat this 10 times with maximum contraction and total relaxation.

SOUND VIBRATION YOGA (MANTRA YOGA)

Mantras (pronounced maantras) are special vibrational sounds. The word *mantra* is generally translated as 'sound vibration', but the literal translation is 'the force which liberates the mind from bondage'. However, mantras have effects on all aspects of the person, not just the mind. Probably the best known of these general mantras is AUM. The mantras used in yoga are formed from combinations of the sounds of the 50 Sanskrit alphabet characters, which correspond to different energy centres in the psychic body, so mantras which are composed of those sounds create vibrations in specific areas of the psychic body. Their vibrations have effects on our physical bodies and our mental functioning.

Physical effects: Because the mantras, when sounded audibly, vibrate the appropriate parts of the physical body, any problems in those parts that respond to vibration improve when the appropriate mantras are repeated. For instance, the last letter of the often-used mantra AUM produces a humming sound, which vibrates the head area. It is an excellent practice for relieving tension headache and chronic sinusitis, but of course it does a lot more than this. Similarly, other mantras especially vibrate the chest area and are good for relieving tension there. In this way, if one knows the area of action of mantras, one will know an appropriate mantra for that area.

Mental effects: If mantra is the force that liberates the mind from bondage, what is this bondage? It has two aspects: impurities (*mala*) and oscillation (*vikshepa*). The impurities are the sum total of all the negative impressions deep in the mind. They are the result of past problems in all areas of our mental being, and relate to such areas of our life as love, joy, security, power, self-esteem, etc. The mantras activate these parts of our mental apparatus and allow these memories to surface, where they can be dealt with and eliminated. The other aspect is the oscillation and distraction of the mind. The internal monologue goes on all day: the desires, the fears, the plans, the disappointments; the mind is never at peace. By repeating the mantras with one-pointed awareness, the oscillations can be quietened, and the mind becomes tranquil and peaceful.

Psychic effects: Mantras can also be used to awaken our psychic potentials, but this subject is better left to be imparted by one's own spiritual master who is experienced in the science of mantra.

The two basic mantras introduced here are AUM and the breath mantra So-Ham. Both are very relaxing and balancing, and are a good preparation for meditation.

AUM practice

Starting with a long breath out, this sound begins with a-a-a, then we close the mouth slowly and progressively, and the sounds o-o-o, then www, then m-m-m blend into each other. We don't try to pronounce those sounds, they just happen as the mouth closes. The sounds at the beginning take up two-thirds of the breath out, and then the m-m-m sound continues for the last third. Then we take another deep breath and repeat it. If we do this for about ten minutes, we experience a tranquil balanced feeling throughout our whole being.

The breath mantra So-Ham

This practice is called *Ajapa Japa*, which means continuous repetition of the mantra. We simply listen to the breath and hear it making the sound of *So* as it goes in, and *Ham* (pronounced Haam) as it goes out. It can be practised anywhere: in a chair, on the floor or in any sitting pose. Important points of ajapa practice are: deep breathing, relaxation and total awareness. We should not let a single breath go unnoticed. Breathing should not be automatic. We must have unceasing awareness of every ingoing and outgoing breath. As soon as the mind wanders, we bring it back to the breath.

The following is an introductory practice derived from Swami Satyananda's book *Dynamics of Yoga*.

Sit in a comfortable position, and just be conscious of every ingoing and outgoing breath for a while.

Now imagine that the ingoing breath goes up from the navel to the throat, and the outgoing breath goes down from the throat to the navel region.

No automatic breathing, but conscious, deep and relaxed breathing.

243

Do not produce any sound while breathing.
Feel the two streams of breath.
Intensify the awareness of prana.
Now add *So-Ham* to this.
As the prana rises with inhalation, feel the vibration of *So*, and as the prana descends with exhalation, feel the vibrations of *Ham*.
Continue to breathe in and out and try to synchronize *So-Ham* with the breath.
So sounds during inhalation and the ascending of the prana in the psychic passage.
Ham sounds during exhalation and the descending of the prana in the psychic passage.
Maintain unceasing awareness of the prana and the mantra.

A few points before we conclude this chapter:
· These few simple practices are really all we need to go a long way on the yoga path. Even the Pawanmuktasana 1 group, called the 'flexibility practices' (for simplicity), do a lot more than their name suggests. They also have a powerful effect on the whole physical/energy/mind system, balancing, freeing blockages, relaxing and strengthening it. Don't underestimate these simple postures.
· In a session of yoga, we usually do the practices in the order in which we have dealt with them here. Asanas first, then any shatkarmas, then pranayamas, then any mudras or bandhas we choose to do, then mantras before the meditation. We may start the session with a few AUMs and a relaxation, but from there the order holds. Then we finish the session with one of the meditation practices.
· The physical practices and the meditation group have been separated into two chapters. In reality, meditation begins with the first posture because an essential part of asanas is the concentration we practise in them.

244

17

Meditation Group of Practices

These are the practices with which we 'go within' and learn who we are. The preliminary ones are the mental relaxation group (*pratyahara*). These practices allow us to 'retreat inside' from the hurly burly of the world and find peace within. This is a necessary beginning for the further practices, which are:

· One-pointed awareness (*dharana*)
· Meditation (*dhyana*)
· Enlightenment (*samadhi*)

These are increasingly deep stages of consciousness, up to samadhi – the transcendental state. Most people are nowhere near attaining that, but the practices 'on the way' are all good for us.

What is meditation?

One dictionary defines meditation as:

1. To focus one's thoughts on, reflect on or ponder over
2. To plan or project in the mind, intend, propose.

In yoga, this is exactly what meditation is not. In fact, it is only when we take our awareness away from those everyday thinking processes that we are able to move into true meditation.

In the *Yoga Sutras* Sage Patanjali tells us that after proper preparation (*yamas, niyamas, asanas and pranayamas*), the next stage is *pratyahara*. This is the 'going in' stage of meditation.

It is the fundamental experience that is central to all the practices of meditation, and it forms the substrata for them all. Put simply: *Pratyahara is our closing off to external perceptions and opening up to internal experiences by letting them come into our awareness.*

Pratyahara gives many of the benefits of meditation just by itself because it brings us into a peaceful relaxed state, free from the activities of the world.

The directions we can take from here are usually considered to be two:

1. Concentrative meditation
2. Opening-up meditation

Concentrative meditation practices try to focus the awareness on one point, and exclude all inputs. This is the method outlined by Sage Patanjali, and in Satyananda Yoga includes *mantra yoga*, *ajapa japa*, and *inner visualization*.

Opening-up meditation, rather than focusing the awareness, allows it to remain open to any input such as thoughts, sounds, emotions, etc. One tries to observe these as an impartial witness or observer, and to allow them to pass without becoming involved. It results in 'clearing out' the lower unconscious mind. Examples of this are observing spontaneous thoughts (*antar mouna*) and spontaneous *inner visualization* – which we will look at in more detail.

These concentrative and opening-up forms are not exclusive of each other; both may need to be done. Indeed, we can't hold the higher levels of concentrative meditation (*dhyana* and *samadhi*) until we have cleared the lower mind to a great extent, because its disturbances force themselves into our awareness when we are trying to concentrate.

BENEFITS OF MEDITATION

The benefits of meditation are experienced throughout every dimension of the person. This can be examined in terms of the five sheaths or koshas.

246

THE PHYSICAL BODY (ANNAMAYA KOSHA)

Muscles and joints relax: Although one usually thinks of the physical practices of yoga as being the ones that help to relax the muscles and joints of the body, the meditation practices help to do this as well. Many people have practised Yoga Nidra, at first physically tense and agitated, and found that at the end of only half an hour the physical tensions have disappeared, even though (and maybe because) the person was not told to relax physically during the practice.

Stress relief – the autonomic-endocrine axis: The practices of meditation have been scientifically proven to move the functioning of the body from the stress response of the sympathetic nervous system and endocrine glands – 'fight or flight' mechanism, towards the relaxed parasympathetic nervous system – 'rest and digest' mechanism. In this way we become much more relaxed physically and mentally, thereby opening the horizons of our life and preventing so many of the illnesses that are caused by stress.

Body armour: As we know, conflicts in the unconscious mind can cause tightening of certain related muscle groups in the body, affecting our posture and facial expression. It is almost as if the body is symbolically protecting itself against possible threats from the original cause of the mental conflict. Perceptive people can actually 'read' the unconscious mental pain of a person by the posture and facial expression of the body. Wilhelm Reich called these tight areas 'character armour' and noted that when the cause of it in the unconscious mind is allowed to surface and is resolved, the tightening goes away. The meditation practices can do just this.

Physical illness: Much scientific research over the years has proved the benefits of meditation in helping to relieve physical illness, and often returning the person to health. This has been shown over a wide range of illnesses, including cancer, cardiovascular disease and respiratory diseases. Of course, meditation is designed to help us evolve to our highest potentials, and is really about wellness rather than

247

illness. However, the same factors that are stopping us from realizing our full potentials are the same ones that cause stress and imbalances in our lives and, as a result, cause most illness and disability. Meditation can certainly help in therapy here, and these illnesses are usually the most difficult to treat by medical means.

THE VITALITY BODY (PRANAMAYA KOSHA)

Energy released from physical tensions → *vitality*: Physical tensions such as those of muscles and joints accumulate a lot of energy, and people are amazed at how much more energetic they feel after a meditation class.

Energy released from mental repressions → *vitality*: The yogis have claimed for thousands of years, and many psychiatrists and psychologists have agreed during the last century, that much of our natural vitality can be 'tied up' in keeping repressed mental material down in the unconscious mind. Just the mere fact of keeping it 'down there' requires energy. They have also noted the increased general vitality that is experienced by people when they can bring the emotionally-loaded unconscious material up into their conscious awareness and discharge it, as happens in psychotherapy and meditation.

THE MIND AND EMOTIONS (MANOMAYA KOSHA)

We will discuss these under the headings of memory, perception, thinking, emotions and behaviour.

Memory

Clearing of repressed memories: Here the meditation practices really come into their own because meditation clears out repressed mental conflicts and neutralizes the emotions that are attached to them. Many of us have had so many of these experiences that we realize this is a great gift that meditation has for the world. As the attached emotions

248

are neutralized, the old memories lose their power to hold us back and we are freed from their 'weight' forever.

So why is yoga such a mind-purifying process? The repressed memories of many of our past experiences – our *samskaras* – carry with them an unconscious emotional charge. They block our ability to evolve to our highest potential, determining our ongoing mental and mood states and the way we interact with our world. If we are to grow, we must neutralize their power.

The majority of the physical techniques of yoga help to bring deeply hidden memories and their emotions to the surface of the mind. Then the meditation practices give the memories a 'screen' onto which they are 'projected' so that we can become aware of them. In meditation we disempower the old samskaras by resurrecting the repressed memories when we are in the *deeply relaxed state* of the *witness*. The resurrection of the memory in that witnessing state makes it 'pliable' and able to be changed by associating it with the disinterested relaxation rather than the old destructive emotion. The experience can then be re-remembered, but this time via the relaxed neutral memory route rather than the stressful adrenalin, noradrenalin route. Then it ceases to have power over us forever.[1]

Gives more positive view of our memories: Because the way we remember our past is dependent on our emotional state when we are trying to remember, if we are in a positive frame of mind, the memories will be the positive ones. If we are in a negative frame of mind, they will be the negative ones. Meditation, by fostering a positive frame of mind, gives us ongoing access to the positive aspects of our past.

Perception

Pratyahara: The different meditation disciplines have their ways of attaining this 'going in' stage of meditation, some easy, some more difficult. Swami Satyananda's practice of Yoga Nidra is an easy way of inducing this state because it comprises a formalized, step-by-step technique of dissociating our awareness from the different outside stimuli in order. At the same time, it interrupts the thought monologue that usually goes on in our mind all day long. If we accomplish these two steps, meditation can go ahead; if we don't, it is impossible.

Awareness of and de-conditioning from habitual ways we perceive our world: Perception is the process whereby a person's sensory stimuli are translated into *organized experiences that have personal meaning for him or her*. Two people walking together along a path take in much the same sights, sounds, etc., but each perceives different aspects of the scene. For instance, one person might 'take in' the beauty of the scenery, while the other 'takes in' any possible dangers that lurk about. In this way, each one of us essentially lives in a 'different world' from the other because what we perceive in any situation depends on our mental programming. The process of meditation allows us to become aware of the processes of our perception so that they cease to become automatic. We can choose what we perceive, whether with eyes closed or open.

Witness begins: As an extension of being aware of our perceptions, we start to go on to the next stage, which is being the *witness* – the *observer* – of our situation, and this develops into witnessing our thought processes, our emotions and our tendencies to behave in certain ways.

Thinking

Attention – taming the monkey: The thinking of most people is 'all over the place', jumping from one idea to another – the reason the yogis refer to the average mind as a 'monkey'. The process of meditation, especially the 'concentrative' forms, gives practice at keeping the attention focused on one thing, be it the parts of the body, the flow of the breath, a mantra, an image, an object of devotion, a candle flame, or something else.

Concentration: When we consider the idea of 'concentrating' in the ordinary sense, we think of the process of thinking intently of an object or situation, where the mind is working intensely. This is not the concentration we try to attain in the dharana stage of meditation. Here the inner perception is on the object of dharana, but the thought process has been largely ignored, and other thoughts that come are just allowed to flow by. We accomplish this in the following way.

Stopping the mind chatter: The mind chatter is the 'internal monologue', the continuous flow of thoughts that goes on in the ordinary person's mind all day long. It doesn't stop from the moment we wake up till we fall asleep. It is changed from time to time by sensations coming in, but it flows on, dominating our mind, emotions, attitudes and behaviour for the whole of our waking life. People are so identified with this thought flow that they may believe it is actually themselves. Often they are surprised at how easy it is to break the flow, and how the mind immediately calms when it happens. Then they realize that the thought patterns with which they identified are just a process, not the person. The meditation practices first cut the internal monologue about outside events, and then they cut the part of it that continues on the basis of memory when the person is 'inside'.

Awareness of thinking habits: As we know, we have developed habits of thinking about our life and our world. Because they are so important in forming the emotions that we experience and the decisions that we make about how we will behave, it is important that we develop the ability to stand back and observe them. Meditation gives us just this ability. We become the witness of our own thinking patterns, and then we have the choice as to whether we want them or not.

Awareness of our ego roles, attitudes and motivations: Many people are strongly identified with their roles in life, their habitual attitudes about themselves, other people, the world around, the reason for life, etc. These attitudes are so much part of each one of us that we take it for granted that they are true. We remain completely oblivious to the fact that other people hold their different attitudes and identify with their roles with the same unshakeable reverence. Because these are so powerful in motivating our ongoing behaviour in life, it is essential that we develop the ability to observe them. Meditation gives us the ability to do this and allows us to put them into perspective.

Emotions

Calming: The processes leading to pratyahara calm negative emotions. They do this in a number of ways. Firstly they allow us to dissociate our awareness from the external inputs that are causing the emotions in the first place. Then they cut the internal monologue that keeps the emotions going. They also lead to physical relaxation, a state that is not compatible with negative emotions. Many people find, even in their first experience of a pratyahara practice such as Yoga Nidra, that uncomfortable emotions just 'melt away'.

Coping with the unconscious emotions: Clearing repressed memories is an important aspect of the purifying power of meditation. The memories have been repressed because the emotions they are covering are painful, but if we are to clear them, we will have to experience those emotions too. Meditation makes this easier for us, by allowing us to be in a neutral emotional state (witness position) to face the unconscious mind. Remember also that physical practices help to put us in an emotionally neutral and balanced state even before the meditation starts.

De-conditioning from habitual emotions: Many people tend to respond to life's inputs with the same old set of emotions, over and over again. Some people respond with anger, some with hurt feelings, some with guilt, some with humour, all to the same situation! Meditation allows us to 'see' where those emotions are coming from. It also develops within us the ability to witness our situation and our responses, and choose more appropriate ones. In addition, it expands our awareness, so that we are able to see the 'bigger picture' of our life, and respond accordingly.

Objective awareness of our desires and repulsions: Raga, attraction to desired objects or situations, and dwesha, repulsion and avoidance of undesired objects or situations, are a part of the process of self-preservation of these bodies of ours. However, in the ordinary lives we live, their hold over us can be inappropriate and lead us into addictive and compulsive behaviours that make life a misery. A fundamental tenet of yoga is that if we are to evolve, we must continuously reduce these desires and repulsions. The meditation practices also allow us to have a more objective view of them; they cease to be automatic, and we can choose how to respond.

Behaviour

Awareness of and de-conditioning from habits of behaviour: We have habitual behaviour patterns too that have become so ingrained that we just take them for granted. Some can be beneficial and some can be quite destructive. Meditation gives us the objectivity to view and assess these. Do we want to continue with them? Or do we want to replace them? The choice is ours.

Automatic improvement in behaviour and relationships: As the meditation and other yoga practices help us to develop, our behaviour and our relationships with other people and with the world around us improve, and we evolve into the more sattwic qualities of vijnanamaya level.

WISDOM–PSYCHIC BODY (VIJNANAMAYA KOSHA)

Clearance of the body-energy-mind: The more we clear the body-energy-mind, the more we experience the qualities of vijnanamaya kosha. These become the basis of our life experience with eyes open or shut. Our whole life becomes meditation. We become physically relaxed, balanced, graceful and 'flowing', and our vitality also becomes balanced and free flowing.

Perception: We perceive the people, objects and situations of our life as they really are, not corrupted by our unconscious blockages or by wishes about how we want them to be.

1. We become more and more the *witness*, and as we do, we become less and less entangled in the situations of life. In this way we are more able to contribute in a helpful, balanced and wise way.
2. Extrasensory perceptions – we are more clearly able to take in information through channels other than the usual five senses
3. Intuition – as we tune into higher sources of information we develop greater ability to reach conclusions and make decisions based on truth.

Reasoning and decision-making: Our reasoning and decision-making are more logical, uncorrupted by repressed mental material, and aided by *intuition* and *precognition*. This leads to wisdom, incorporating right understanding and discernment (*viveka*).

Unconditional love: Instead of trying to love, we *become* the love that was already inside us. It just flows out of us in the same unconditional way as the perfume wafts from a flower.

Compassion: Because of the release of our love, we relate to others and to planet Earth, in a kind, non-harming way. As a result we become more ethical in the way we deal with our world and the individuals in it.

Communication: We relate to other people with free communication, social adeptness and harmony.

Inner security: Because we have essentially eliminated the sources of our old irrational insecurities, we become secure within ourselves. This allows us to appreciate the beauty of life. We also become less acquisitive and less possessive of material things (*asteya* and *aparigraha*), and less attached to and entangled in the things and people around us (*vairagya*). In the same way, because of our security we have the courage to be truthful (*satya*), and it becomes natural for us to be so.

Spontaneous joy: We experience joy in life, and relate to situations and other people with humour, optimism and a positive attitude.

Ability to accomplish good work: Our life flows with the ability to accomplish good work in a selfless way, unimpeded by blockages of the lower mind. This results in good self-esteem and motivation. At a higher level we perceive the hand of divine grace in our endeavours and feel ourselves to be an instrument of that grace.

BLISS-ENLIGHTENMENT DIMENSION
(ANANDAMAYA KOSHA)

The vast majority of our human race are still slowly progressing in the lower koshas and don't even have a glimmer of the exalted fate in store for us at the level of anandamaya kosha. Ultimately, however, according to yoga, it is the destiny of us all.

To quote Swami Satyananda in *Meditations from the Tantras*:

The culmination of meditation is self-realization. This occurs when the higher mind is transcended. The consciousness leaves the exploration of the mind and identifies with the central core of one's existence, the Self. At this point it becomes pure consciousness. When a person achieves Self-realization, it means that he has contacted his central being and now identifies his existence, his life, from the viewpoint of the Self and not from the standpoint of the ego. When he acts from the centre of his being, the body and mind operate almost as separate entities. The mind and body cease to be real to him; they are merely manifestations of the Self, his true identity. So it can be seen that the aim of meditation is to explore the different regions of the mind and eventually transcend the mind completely.

THREE PRACTICES

Yoga Nidra

Please get ready for yoga nidra.

Lie down on your back in shavasana, the corpse pose, with the feet a little apart, the hands by the sides with the palms facing upwards, and the eyes closed. Make the body as comfortable as possible and then try to allow the body to remain perfectly still.

Develop awareness of the body from the top of the head to the tips of the toes. Complete stillness and complete awareness of the whole body.

Continue your awareness of the whole body, the whole body, the whole body.

Mentally say to yourself: 'I am aware, I am going to practise yoga nidra, I will not sleep, I will remain awake throughout the whole practice'. (*pause*)

Now begin to rotate your awareness throughout your whole physical body.

Repeat the different parts of the body in your mind and simultaneously become aware of that part of the body. You can also, if you choose, visualize that part of the body in your mind, but don't concentrate too hard, and don't try to relax the part, just have an easy awareness.

(*Right side*)

Become aware of the right hand thumb, second finger, third finger, fourth finger, fifth finger, palm, back of the hand, wrist, lower arm, elbow, upper arm, shoulder, armpit, right side of the body, the waist, right hip, right thigh, knee, calf muscle, ankle, heel, sole, right big toe, second toe, third toe, fourth toe, fifth toe.

(*Left side*)

Become aware of the left hand thumb, second finger, third finger, fourth finger, fifth finger, palm, back of the hand, wrist, lower arm, elbow, upper arm, shoulder, armpit, left side of the body, the waist, left hip, left thigh, knee, calf muscle, ankle, heel, sole, left big toe, second toe, third toe, fourth toe, fifth toe.

(*Back*)

Now come to the back. Become aware of the right buttock, left buttock, small of the back, right side of the back, left side of the back, centre of the back, right shoulder blade, left shoulder blade, centre of the shoulder blades.

Now become aware of the spine from the bottom right up to the top, the whole back together, back of the neck, back of the head.

(*Front*)

Now go to the top of the head, forehead, both sides of the head, right eyebrow, left eyebrow, eyebrow centre, right eyelid, left eyelid, the right eye, the left eye. right ear, left ear, right cheek, left cheek, nose, tip of the nose, upper lip, lower lip, chin, throat, right side of the chest, left side of the chest, centre of the chest, the abdomen, the right side of the abdomen, the left side of the abdomen, the upper abdomen, the navel, the lower abdomen, the pelvic area.

(*Major parts*)

The whole right leg, the whole left leg, both legs together. (*pause*) The whole right arm, the whole left arm, both arms together. (*pause*)

The whole of the back, buttocks, spine, shoulder blades, the whole of the front, abdomen, chest, the whole of the back and front together, the whole of the head, the whole body together, the whole body together, the whole body together.

(*You may repeat one or two rounds of this rotation of awareness through the body parts, gradually decreasing speed.*)

Now just become aware of the natural breath, aware that the breath is flowing in and flowing out. There is no need to make the breathing happen, just be aware of the natural breath. Become aware of its rhythm – whether it is fast or slow, shallow or deep, but there is no need to change it – only awareness. Just remain aware of the breath for a short while . . .

Now begin to count mentally each respiration; inhalation and exhalation count mentally as *one*. Count the breaths from 54 to zero, remaining aware of each breath and number. If you miss one breath, then you should start again.

When you finally reach zero, become aware of your physical body lying on the floor; awareness of your physical body from top to toe. Then become aware of the room and your surroundings.

Then start moving your body and stretching yourself. When you are wide awake, sit up slowly and open your eyes.

The practice of yoga nidra is now complete.

Internal Visualization

We may add this practice to the above Yoga Nidra after the rotation of awareness on the body parts.

Now become aware of the flow of the breath through the nostrils. Just allow the breath to flow as it will. You don't have to change the breathing, just let it happen.

You will notice that as the breath flows in, the nostrils become a little cooler, and as the breath flows out, they become a little warmer. That is quite natural; it goes on all the time. Just let it go on, but remain aware of it.

Now try to imagine that the breath is actually flowing in through the left nostril and out through the right nostril, then back in through the right nostril and out through the left, then back in through the left nostril and so on. Alternate nostril psychic breathing – a practice that produces perfect balance.

At first it is just imagination, but after a while it may feel as if it is really happening. Just continue in that way, left to right, right to left, left to right, etc., for a few minutes . . . Now allow the alternate nostril breathing to continue by itself, feel as if it is going on automatically . . . the alternate breathing is just going on by itself, maintaining you in perfect balance. At the same time, just look at the inside of your forehead, as if there is a screen there, as if it is a movie screen, or a TV screen . . . just watch it, and see if anything appears there.

At first the screen may appear blank, but keep watching it. If anything appears, just observe it and let it go. Be like the witness or the observer, just seeing it, and then letting it go. Try not to think about anything you see, only about the flow of the breath through the alternate nostrils.

Remain watching the screen, and feeling the alternate nostril breathing for five or ten minutes, then become aware of your physical body; awareness of your physical body from top to toe. Then become aware of the room and your surroundings.

Then start moving your body and stretching yourself, and when you are wide awake, sit up slowly and open your eyes.

The practice of internal visualization is now complete.

Thought Observation

We may add this practice to the above Yoga Nidra after the rotation of the awareness on the body parts.

Just become aware of thoughts, the spontaneous thought process, thoughts that come and go of their own accord.

You don't have to bring in a thought flow, just let it come spontaneously, and let it go of its own accord.

Try to remain a silent witness of every thought that is going through your mind. When you become aware of a particular thought, you will have to say to your mind, 'Yes, I am thinking about this and that'.

If the mind supposedly becomes free of thoughts, you should try to become aware of that state also. There can come a stage of thoughtlessness even in the case of a beginner.

You are looking at the process of your thoughts and you are sure of the thoughts that are passing through.

You should remain alert throughout. The purpose of this is not to check the thoughts but to observe the thoughts. If sometimes you become absentminded, and then you revive your awareness, say to yourself, 'Well, I became absentminded for some time, and during those moments I was thinking of this and that'.

But please try to be aware of all thoughts that are spontaneously coming up, that are manifesting in your awareness.

Bad thoughts and good thoughts will come; they should come and you should let them come. If they come, look at them indifferently, with absolute detachment, as a witness or as a spectator.

Continue with this for a few minutes more, then become aware of your breathing, then of your physical body; awareness of your physical body from top to toe. Then become aware of the room and your surroundings.

Then start moving your body and stretching yourself, and when you are wide awake, sit up slowly and open your eyes.

The practice of thought observation is now complete.

This brings us to the end of our chapters on the yoga techniques. Most of the practices were taken or derived from: *Asana Pranayama Mudra Bandha, Meditations from the Tantras, Dynamics of Yoga* and *Yoga Nidra* by Swami Satyananda Saraswati, all published by Yoga Publications Trust, Munger, Bihar, India (see Bibliography).

259

An Overview
of Yoga and
our Evolvement

18

How Yoga Evolves Vicious Circles into Virtuous Circles

What is the fundamental reality that governs whether we evolve or go the other way? Some people just seem to go up; their timing is excellent, the right people and the right things come their way, they are surrounded by smiling people who love them, and they even maintain abundant good health. Life for them and the people they influence just gets better and better. Good luck? Maybe, but . . .

Other people, who grow up in the same kind of situation, just go from one disaster to another; things rarely come together for them, nobody is there to help them when they need it, their lives are a long string of fractured relationships, and to make matters worse they are sick most of the time. Their life just gets worse and worse as they are stuck down in the morass of trouble. Bad luck? Possibly, but . . . Why do they get stuck? Read on, maybe this has something to do with it all:

Sri Krishna said in the *Bhagavad Gita* (14:18):

Those who are seated in Sattwa go upwards; the Rajasic dwell in the middle; and the tamasic, abiding in the function of the lowest Guna, go downwards.

How does this happen? Maybe the main causes are the *vicious circles* that are the curse of tamas, and the *virtuous circles* that are the blessing of sattwa. What is a vicious circle? *Webster's Dictionary* says: "A vicious circle is a chain of events

263

in which the response to a difficulty creates a new problem that aggravates that original difficulty."

The virtuous circles of sattwa do just the opposite; the response to an occurrence creates a positive result that improves the whole situation, and as it repeats, the whole thing becomes better and better.

How do these express themselves in life?

In rajas the vicious and virtuous circles are about equal, so they average out as Sri Krishna implied, but things go from bad to worse in tamas and from good to better to best in sattwa. This is why the people who get stuck in tamasic qualities in some of their personality aspects need to become involved in yoga to lift themselves up out of that morass.

As we have more experience in yoga and observe other people who are practising yoga, we see many examples of the ways yoga changes vicious circles of our life into virtuous circles, and how this allows us to get out of the downward spirals of tamas, and evolve towards our best. Throughout this book we have seen many examples of this. What are these vicious and virtuous circles, and how do they come about? Let us look at them in terms of the ten avenues of expression we have been discussing.

In tamas the vicious circles go on three levels of the individual: the physical body (*annamaya kosha*), the vitality body (*pranamaya kosha*) and the mental body (*manomaya kosha*). The same applies to the virtuous circles in sattwa, which also has the benefits of the intellectual level (*vijnanamaya kosha*) and the bliss level (*anandamaya kosha*).

Our basic mind aspects of manomaya kosha consist of the following:

· Ahamkara – the sense of 'I'-ness
· Chitta – our memory
· Manas – our perceptions, thinking and emotions
· Buddhi – the lower levels of our higher mind.

THE SENSE OF 'I'-NESS (AHAMKARA)

The vicious circles of tamas

At the tamasic level, people experience themselves as isolated from others. They may be alienated if there is a lot of fear, or maybe even paranoid if they project anger. Vicious circles can come from their disregard for the needs or rights of others because of their emotional distance from them. As a result other people retaliate with their version of disregard, and this bounces backwards and forwards, getting worse as it goes along. Yoga relieves the emotional tensions that feed the feelings of isolation and so improves sociability. Another source of vicious circles in this modality is the low self-esteem that people at this level feel. This leads to lack of confidence, which in turn leads to failure and more loss of self-esteem. The great yogic panacea for this is karma yoga, where self-esteem is guarded by non-attachment to outcomes, and is increased by the good work they are doing.

In some people the problem may not just be isolation, it may be alienation. Very tamasic levels of 'I'-ness can give a strong experience of 'self-reference', in which they imagine that events happening 'out there' are in some way referring to them. They may misinterpret the innocent actions, remarks or gestures of other people as intentional slights, insults or contempt directed at them. One can imagine the problems that can arise from this. Yoga creates a general reduction in negative emotions that can help people in this state; for instance, balancing ida and pingala is also very important.

The virtuous circles of sattwa

In the sattwic state the 'I'-ness is not isolation, it is union – an experience of 'I' as a part of 'us'. There is an awareness of 'we' rather than 'me', so this unitive relationship with other people raises our compassion, helpfulness, kindness, cooperation and friendship. Usually these are returned by the other people, so we are receiving all these beneficial 'gifts' from those around us. This benevolence builds up in the form of a virtuous circle for all concerned.

PERCEPTION

The vicious circles of tamas

People don't usually realize this, but what goes into forming our perceptions of what we sense outside is what is inside us! So what I 'see' out there is to a great extent created from what is going on inside my own mind. Freud called this process 'projection' and was interested in the 'sick' stuff we 'see' out there because it is really in here. The exploiter sees the world as exploitative or exploitable, the hostile person sees it as hostile, the 'power freak' sees power games everywhere and so on. Then the person's thinking, emotions and behaviour will be at least partly determined by these perceptions. The vicious circle comes from the negative perceptions of out there, arousing negative responses inside, which increase the hypervigilance, and this results in projecting more negativity out there. By eliminating the negative content 'in here', yoga improves the quality of our perceptions of the world.

The virtuous circles of sattwa

We can experience our world as frightening, angry, sad, power crazy, etc., because we project these tamasic qualities from inside our own natures. However, if we have sattwic qualities dominant in our natures, we may project those too; we have a positive experience of the world, so we respond to it in a like way. When you are feeling loving, you see love and lovability in the world. When you are feeling happy, everybody seems to be smiling at you as you go about the day and the sun seems to be shining even on a cloudy day. Everything around us responds to us in kind, so the quality of our experience goes up, and the whole thing grows in the positive way of a virtuous circle.

MEMORIES

The vicious circles of tamas

The things that we remember most easily at any moment correspond with our current feeling state. If we are feeling depressed, the memories we have will be about all the hurts and disappointments of our past. If we are anxious, our memories will be about all the frightening occurrences in our life; if angry, all the affronts and anger by other people will be foremost. Now remember that our assessment of what we can expect in the future is based mainly on past experiences. So the bad memories of a person's past experiences in any personality aspect (insecurity, material losses, sadness, helplessness, hurt, grief, isolation, etc.) will paint an equally bleak future. We become pessimistic, give up trying, and become stuck in the inertia of tamas. Also bad memories lead to bad behaviour, then retaliation from outside gives more bad memories.

The virtuous circles of sattwa

Because the things we remember most easily at any moment correspond with our current feeling state, our feelings in the sattwic states of our different personality aspects will be positive ones, so they will evoke positive memories. These will transfer into the future as optimism, so we will be motivated to do more in the sattwic style of nurturing ourselves and helping other people and the world, with the obvious virtuous circles that ensue from those activities.

THINKING

The vicious circles of tamas

The thinking *content* at this level is based on perceptions from outside or mental rumination from inside. Tamasic perceptions cause negative thinking, which then joins in with the negative rumination and it all goes from bad to worse. It feeds on itself; for instance, building up a little insult or rejection into a major catastrophe.

The *quality* of the person's thinking at this level is also poor. It is full of irrational judgements, distortions of logic, denial, justifications, excuses, etc. We can imagine just how disabling this poor quality thinking can be.

The virtuous circles of sattwa

1. *Thinking*: At the sattwic levels, our instinctual thinking is very much under the sway of our higher thinking, so the selfishness of 'me first and only' that is common at the lower levels of the gunas is not active. Rather, the thinking is at least from the intellectual (buddhi) level, so it is ethical and considerate of other people.

2. *Intellect*: The sattwic levels use the intellect, sometimes to high levels, to cope with our lives. The quality of the thinking is good, without the irrationality, poor judgements, illogical distortions, justifications and excuses for problematic behaviour, etc., of tamas. Also, the content of thinking that is provoked by our experiences of our world is good because our experiences are good. Similarly, the content of our ruminations will be positive because it is a blend of thinking about our experiences and of our memories. As all these augment our emotions and behaviour, their positive quality leads to positive outcomes.

3. *Intuition*: At the high levels of sattwa our judgements, decisions, etc., about any aspects of our life will be augmented by intuition and wisdom. Those decisions will be right, and the consequences that flow from them will be the best in the circumstances. As a result we will be creating win-win situations, with all the advantages that come from those, including virtuous circle outcomes.

EMOTIONS

The vicious circles of tamas

The vicious circles of the negative emotions are well known, and are the cause of many diseases as well as much unhappiness and strife. All emotions can have a negative complexion, but to mention just the three main ones, the vicious circles are:

Anxiety → symptoms → fear of illness/madness/death → more anxiety
Anger → aggression → social conflict → more anger
Dejection → inertia → failure → more dejection → maybe depression

We can see that any of these can build up and up, becoming worse as time goes on. This is a typical example of, "the tamasic, abiding in the function of the lowest guna, go downwards." (*Bhagavad Gita* 14:18)

Yoga practices can break these vicious circles, starting the person on the upward path of confidence, kindness and joy.

The virtuous circles of sattwa

At the sattwic levels the *emotions* we experience such as fear, anger, remorse, regret, etc., are reality based, such as reasonable anger at injustices, or regret over a personal act or omission. And they lead to action to try to reverse the situation, such as action to stop an injustice. Mahatma Gandhi and Nelson Mandela are beautiful examples of reasonable anger that worked. Or we make amends and resolve not to repeat the inappropriate action.

The sattwic *feelings* we experience are the positive ones such as security, joy, humour, confidence, good self-esteem, love, compassion, kindness and empathy. As well as making us feel wonderful, they also lead us to beneficial behaviour, and the virtuous circles that arise from that.

BEHAVIOUR

The vicious circles of tamas

The behaviour engendered by *anxiety* will include withdrawal, dependency and addiction. The vicious circle here is the way the sense of helplessness in the face of the fear produces more fear. In addition, the methods we use to try to relieve

269

anxiety, such as addiction and dependency, create problems of their own.

The behaviour arising from *anger* is usually vengeance, aggression, violence, etc., and the vicious circle here is the retaliation from the people we have hurt, which causes us to be more angry and aggressive.

The behaviour from the *dejection/depression* vicious circle is *withdrawal*, which results in loneliness and the feeling of being unloved, and *inertia*, which causes our inability to attend to our responsibilities, with the guilt that then results.

Self-fulfilling prophecies: Another problem is that tamasic interactions with the world attract responses from other people which justify all the above attitudes, and this perpetuates them as self-fulfilling 'prophecies'. It can happen in all the tamasic situations, but a good example is that of paranoia where the person believes that they are the victims of persecution from 'out there'.

How does paranoia happen? The paranoid person denies their own anger and projects it onto the other person, so they see the other person as dangerous to them. In defence, they retaliate with anger and threats of their own. This does make the other person (who was originally neutral or even friendly) angry and defensive. Thus the paranoid person's original assessment of the other person as being angry and dangerous is proved 'right' – it has become a self-fulfilling prophecy and justifies further aggression.

Another problem here is that the paranoid person cannot see their responsibility for this trouble because of the lack of insight of people at the tamasic level. In addition, the crux of paranoia is that the problem is perceived 'out there', so they feel, 'It's not me, it's him!' If such a relationship continues, it can become very difficult, or even a disaster. Psychiatrists and others who have dealt with paranoid people will recognize this difficult situation, and the intractable morass of vicious circles it is.

270

The virtuous circles of sattwa

We see the positive outcomes of our sattwic attitudes most clearly in the area of our behaviour. If we interact with people with love, joy, kindness, consideration, helpfulness and the other sattwic qualities, they respond to us in the same way, and the whole relationship continues to improve as virtuous circles. Even if the other person does not respond in this way, for instance if they exploit our kindness, our vairagya allows us to 'let it pass', and the empathy that comes from sattwa allows us to understand them. This can even help them too.

THE PHYSICAL BODY

The vicious circles of tamas

Physical difficulties are caused by the mental and emotional states that usually accompany the tamasic level of functioning. They are stress, tension, dejection, anger, various imbalances, etc., which give rise to typical psychosomatic illnesses, immune system dysfunction, organ damage and a vast array of symptoms. One becomes worried or depressed, and the anxiety or depression causes more of the abnormalities in the body. In this way, it goes from bad to worse, in a typical vicious circle. The usual tamasic lifestyles and intake of food and drinks also have a detrimental effect on the body, but as yoga has a positive effect on our lifestyle the deleterious effects on the body, mind and vitality are reversed.

The virtuous circles of sattwa

The lifestyle, thinking and emotions of sattwa are conducive to health and longevity. The person is likely to experience robust good health and satisfaction with their body, and these reflect back onto the body as positive influences.

THE VITALITY BODY

The vicious circles of tamas

When the person is in the state of lethargy and inertia that is tamas, they stop doing things, sit around, watch all the bad news on TV, become depressed and more and more physically inactive. This allows their energy to run down even more, so the vicious circle forms.

The virtuous circles of sattwa

Sattwa encourages us to be optimistic, enthusiastic, active, and to get out and do things, usually for the benefit of others. This keeps our vitality high and encourages ongoing activity, which keeps the vitality flowing.

All the sattwic elements combine to create the way we behave in our world, and they determine the virtuous circles that form around us. As yoga lifts us up out of the more tamasic levels, sattwa increasingly becomes our way of life. The beauty of this is that, as Sri Krishna said, we "*go upwards*", and if we look at the process clearly, it is obvious that the whole thing accelerates in the direction of our evolvement.

19

Yogic Mechanisms of Evolvement

In practical yoga psychology we have a many levelled method to assess ourselves, for example, our strengths, weaknesses, ambitions and needs. We can then apply our knowledge of yogic practices and lifestyle to evolve our personality. The koshas give us the big picture. The different sheaths of the person – physical body, energy body, mind body, wisdom body and bliss body – are affected by all the yoga practices. If we help one of the koshas, the positive effect will ripple through to the others. However, some practices, and indeed lifestyles, are more specific for certain koshas. To put it simply, the *postures* are for the physical body, the *pranayamas* are for the energy body, and the *meditation* group are for the mind group of koshas.

Besides learning to appreciate our own development in the area of the koshas, we can next assess which chakras are most activated by recognizing their qualities in our lives, and then how evolved (tamasic, rajasic or sattwic) these qualities are at present. In this chapter there is a practical breakdown of which techniques will affect us in these dimensions.

THE CHAKRA SYSTEMS AND THEIR ACTIVATION

The basic *aspects* of the chakra systems, which form the foundation stones of our personality, are security, joy/sexuality, power, love, communication and intellect/intuition.

We try to develop these in a balanced way, and most of the practices contribute to this by *activating* their respective chakra systems.

Performed practices

Postures (*asanas*): The mooladhara chakra system is stimulated by any postures that act on the area of the perineum, or the many practices that involve the legs and feet. The swadhisthana chakra system is activated by postures for the lower part of the trunk, especially the lumbo-sacral area of the spine. Manipura is activated by any of the postures for the middle part of the trunk, especially the thoraco-lumbar area. Similarly, anahata is activated by postures for the thoracic spine, and the shoulders and arms, vishuddhi by postures for the lower neck area and upper arms, and ajna by postures for the upper neck.

We should note that some series such as the flexibility practices (Pawanmuktasana 1) and salute to the sun (Surya Namaskara) activate all or most of the chakras. On a more subtle level, when we are performing the postures, we may concentrate on a particular chakra and maybe repeat a mantra. This will have an additional effect on awakening the chakras.

Cleansing practices (*shatkarmas*): Foremost here is the series of five asanas for the intestinal/bowel wash (*shankha-prakshalana*) practice, which have a good all round effect on all of the chakras. Shankhaprakshalana combined with the nasal wash and regurgitative cleansing activates all chakras. The nasal wash (*neti*) especially activates ajna. Regurgitative cleansing (*kunjal*) activates manipura.

Breath practices (*pranayamas*): These are primarily to do with vitality, but in the course of their action some awaken chakras; for instance, the humming bee breath (*bhramari pranayama*) stimulates ajna chakra.

Attitudes and locks (*mudras and bandhas*): One of their effects is to stimulate chakras. For example, the perineum contraction (*moola bandha*) stimulates mooladhara chakra; *namaskara mudra*, as in the first position of salute to the sun, stimulates anahata chakra; and *shambhavi mudra* (gazing at the eyebrow centre) activates ajna chakra.

Mental deep relaxation (pratyahara): Rotating the awareness around the different parts of the body in turn, as we do in Yoga Nidra, stimulates the chakras in a fully balanced way.

Meditation: Often in the dharana practices we will concentrate on the chakras. Even though we are not doing anything physical at the time, the chakras are stimulated. This principle forms the basis of many of the yoga series, right up to the most powerful combinations such as kundalini-kriya yoga.

Lifestyle

Interactions within our life produce a variety of experiences relating to all the different aspects of the chakras. Each of these will activate its appropriate chakra circuit. If we have enough life experience, and don't just live like hermits, there will be good balance of these activations. Karma yoga is excellent here because if we are doing it right, we are fully aware of what is going on, and can keep track of the chakra-related qualities of our personality that are having their 'buttons pressed', and learn from that.

EVOLVING THE QUALITIES OF THE CHAKRA SYSTEMS

This is an enormous area, which forms the crux of the whole of yoga, and indeed the reason for our being here in this life. The fundamental questions are:

· What are some of the factors that lift us up into sattwa and allow us to stay there?
· What are some of the factors that drag us down into tamas and hold us there?
· How can the practices of yoga maximize the former and minimize the latter?

Although there is no short answer, we will summarize it as follows:

PERFORMED PRACTICES

Postures (*asanas*)

There are many ways we can use asanas to break out of the grip of tamas and rajas. The asanas stimulate the chakra systems directly, which results in the repressed memories of negative experiences in the unconscious mind becoming available to our awareness. Thus we can process them in meditation and eliminate their degrading influence on us.

We must keep up our vitality to evolve the qualities of our personality. The postures raise our energy directly, and they also unblock energy that is caught up in stressed parts of the body.

Stretching of the muscles eliminates the 'tension feedback' and reduces this source of mental tensions. Physical relaxation produces emotional and mental relaxation, so it eliminates the vicious circles of accumulating mental tensions in our lives.

The physical balancing of both sides of the body helps to balance ida and pingala because the feed-in to the two sides of the brain is equal.

Asanas break the vicious circle of negative mind-states that lead to abnormal body posture, which then feeds back into the mind to perpetuate that mental state and hold us down in tamas or rajas.

Flexibility of the body produces flexibility of the mind, so we are able to assess our negative attitudes, etc., and change them. Relaxation produced by a yoga session lasts way beyond the session and becomes an ongoing state as we continue over time with our practices. It breaks the vicious circles such as *anxiety → tension → fear → anxiety*.

Toning is the opposite of relaxation. Asanas tone the body, which overcomes the flaccidity caused by depressed emotions and mind-states. This helps to reverse another vicious circle of: *depression → stooped flaccid posture → dejection → more depression*.

Strength is increased by the appropriate physical practices, and this overcomes the feeling of weakness that leads to the inability to pull ourselves out of the morass of tamas. The physical asanas help us to develop general fitness; we feel better in an ongoing way, and 'grow' from there.

Because the physical symptoms of anxiety and tension that accompany stress make the stress worse, when we relieve those symptoms with yoga the stress is relieved, turning a vicious circle into a virtuous circle. This is augmented by another virtuous circle created by the sense of mastery people develop when they can reverse their own stress and anxiety symptoms. The anxiety is dissolved, replacing helplessness (which worsens the stress and anxiety) with the self-esteem of independence, and the joy of throwing away the tranquillizers.

When we are doing asanas, we concentrate only on what we are doing. This concentration breaks the negative internal monologue, and really constitutes the first step in our meditation process. People think that meditation starts when we close our eyes, but it really starts as soon as we concentrate enough to break the internal monologue. It can happen very early in the yoga class, or during the normal course of the day if we choose.

Many of the yoga practices, including the asanas, help to cure or relieve physical illness that is impeding our process of evolving, so they open the way for us to grow in this way.

Cleansing practices (*shatkarmas*)

The cleansing and maintenance of the physical body has an immediate positive effect on our wellbeing. In the process, the mind is also cleansed because the shatkarmas have a direct effect on activating and eliminating unconscious negative material, and so purifying the mind.

Breath practices (*pranayamas*)

Swami Satyananda writes in *Asana Pranayama Mudra Bandha*:

Pranayama utilizes breathing to influence the flow of prana in the nadis or energy channels of the pranamaya kosha or energy body . . . The techniques provide the method whereby the life force can be activated and regulated in order to go beyond one's normal boundaries or limitations and attain a higher state of vibratory energy.

In addition to this process of evolution at the energy level, pranayamas have some immediate effects that help us to attain and maintain a positive balanced state of mind, increased vitality and relaxation. Frontal brain cleansing breath (*kapalbhati*) is a forced exhalation breathing which expands the vitality *physically* and *mentally* as well as clearing the mind. Simple breath awareness, the humming bee breath (*bhramari*) and the soft snoring psychic breath (*ujjayi*) are very relaxing practices.

Attitudes and locks (*mudras and bandhas*)
Mudras and bandhas activate chakras and so play a part in purifying the unconscious mental and emotional samskaras that lie behind those chakra systems. In this way they help to evolve the related qualities.

Mantra yoga
From mantras we get all the benefits – physical, mental and emotional – that we get from the other practices. Repeating mantras, whether aloud or mentally, is relaxing and gives us a positive frame of mind and emotions. It is thus a good preparation for meditation practices.

Mantra is very good for stopping the mind when we want to. It interrupts the internal monologue and if we regularly use our personal mantra, with which we are very familiar, that 'thought train' can be instantly obliterated. Mantras can also put a gap between: *perception* → *thought*; *thought* → *emotion*; *emotion* → *action*; so that at any of these points we can stop and decide what is the best thing to do.

278

The sounds of the mantras activate the chakras, and we can easily feel this. The mantras stimulate, balance and clear the blockages of the whole chakra circuits, leading to the evolvement of the chakra qualities. Mantras just seem like sounds made by the voice, and we can feel their physical effect, but they affect all levels of the individual at the same time, right up to the highest and most subtle levels of consciousness.

Mental deep relaxation (*pratyahara*) and meditation (*dhyana*)

The practice of going inside is of fundamental importance in the process of evolving the aspects of the personality through yoga. In Chapter 17 we dealt with the positive effects at the levels of the five koshas. What are some of the ways that meditation techniques can help us to evolve the different aspects of our personality?

When we develop the ability to relax our mind at will, it gives us a sense of mastery over the vagaries of the mind, and allows us to maintain it in a positive state. Many people don't know they can withdraw from the incessant barrage of external stimuli, or that they can then control their mind when 'inside'. It comes as a pleasant surprise when we realize how easy it is, and how much power it gives us to contribute to our own personal evolvement.

We have mentioned many times how yoga can stop or control the constant stream of thoughts that goes on inside us. The problem with this incessant rumination is that it influences all the ten ways of our expression, often in a negative way, and that keeps us down in the lower levels. Just this simple skill of blocking the internal monologue often signals the start of our ability to evolve ourselves.

Another factor that holds us down in the lower levels is simply lack of concentration. The mind refuses to stay on one point and deal with what needs to be dealt with, so we keep failing in our various endeavours. The meditation practices train us in concentration, and this ability continues long after the session of meditation has finished.

By going into pratyahara, we can access the unconscious mind to put in positive affirmations and resolutions (*sankalpas*) to improve our life. Eliminating the repressions that are holding down unwanted memories in the unconscious mind frees vitality that we can then use for the evolving process. Meditation clears out repressed mental conflicts and neutralizes the emotions attached to them. The old memories lose their power to hold us back and we are freed from them forever. This is an instant step up in our evolvement.

With meditation we develop our ability to be the *witness* – the *observer* – of our situation, of our thought processes, emotions, of our tendencies to behave in certain ways. This allows us to control these for the better.

Developing the *witness* position also allows us to observe our ego roles and to detach ourselves from dependence on them. Our patterns of habitual thinking, our attitudes and our motivations also start to become clear to us. This ability to perceive and later control these usually automatic processes gives us the ability to assess their usefulness and the option to choose what to do about them in the interests of our evolvement.

The compulsive desires inherent in our attraction to desired objects or situations (*raga*) and our repulsion from and avoidance of undesired objects or situations (*dwesha*) keep us 'running off' in all directions. The resulting addictions to getting pleasures and avoiding unwanted situations can hold us down in tamas. When we realize this, meditation can give us a witnessing overview and allow us to choose whether to 'run' or not, and 'which way'.

Negative emotions feed on themselves and can keep us in a constant state of tamas. The calming of negative emotions that occurs from meditation is often the first time people realize that they can control them and begin their process of evolution by yoga. Meditation also deals with the spontaneous upsurge of emotions from the unconscious mind that plagues some people, by eliminating the emotionally loaded repressed conflicts that are causing them.

We also start to recognize that some of our habitual behaviour patterns may be of great benefit to us, for instance, smiling at people, or speaking kindly. But some can be harmful and keep us down; some can be downright destructive and dangerous to ourselves and other people. Meditation gives an overview of these from the witness position. It allows us to firstly identify behaviour that has caused us trouble so we can try to rectify the situation. We can resolve not to let it happen again, and eventually we are able to recognize the problem behaviour before it starts and choose what to do about it.

As we clear the blockages to our evolution through the avenues mentioned above, we start to experience the qualities of vijnanamaya kosha. In the meditation process we have higher experiences into the 'super-conscious' mind and this starts to flow over into the rest of the day. We can perceive the world in a realistic way; we develop better reasoning, discrimination, discernment and decision-making. Our unconditional love and compassion grow, we communicate with others better, we have increased personal security, increased joy and a better ability to accomplish good work. Obviously this all creates virtuous circles that accelerate our evolvement in an ever-growing wave.

LIFESTYLE PRACTICES

General lifestyle considerations

Obviously we are looking for a lifestyle that enhances our exposure to situations that uplift us, and avoiding any aspects of our lifestyle that degrade us. This really means a simple lifestyle, maintaining positive input, keeping out negative input, watching our thinking patterns to keep positive, and removing the negative mind-stuff. Some of these require the other yoga practices, but the right general lifestyle will enhance and establish even these aspects. In Chapter 11, we emphasized five main areas.

1. *Simplicity*: This includes efficiency, regularity, moderation and activity. Many people have unnecessarily complicated lives that drag them down. To evolve out of this, they need to consider their real needs and take steps to clear some of these burdens.

2. *Physical intake*: This includes mainly foods, drugs and pollution. If we are to lift ourselves out of the quagmire of tamas or the dizzy pursuit of the desires of rajas, we need to assess and try to adjust our lifestyle towards sattwa.

3. *Mental and emotional intake*: Some people are meticulous about the quality of their physical lifestyle, but constantly allow negative input into their mind. With yoga we develop the ability to stand back and look at what we are allowing in. Is it lifting us up or pulling us down?

4. *People in our lives*: Who have we allowed to become part of our life? Obviously there are people with whom we have karma, people we have to care for, especially children and other family members; they should be there. Similarly, we can't eliminate every difficult individual from our sphere; we may even have a lot to learn from them. But some people only drag us down and stop us from evolving. We need to take a good look at this, to promote positive people in our life and avoid the negative ones.

5. *Ethics and personal wellbeing*: This is dealt with by the yamas and niyamas.

6. *Making an inventory*: I am not recommending that we escape to a cave, away from all those terrible influences; we need our world with which to interact and evolve. However, useless and corrupting elements of our lifestyle can unnecessarily hold us back in our quest to evolve. We need to look at our interactions, maybe write them down and assess what they are doing for us or to us in this quest. This is made easier by the new perspectives we gain as we perform the other yoga practices.

Raja yoga – yamas and niyamas

Sage Patanjali was being quite pragmatic when he advised us to observe the *yamas*, or self-restraints and ethics, and the *niyamas*, or personal codes, as the first two requirements on his eight stage path to enlightenment. Our peace of mind is disturbed if we have in our past a long string of hurts to others, lies, thefts, attachments and possibly awkward sexual encounters. These can stand in the way of attaining meditation and evolving our potentials. Until we can rise above these behaviours, they will cause emotional disturbances within us that block our path upward.

In addition, at some level of our consciousness, under the influence of our higher selves, we *know* what is right and wrong, we know what is ethical and what is unethical, and we know when we are hurting another individual in some way. No matter if we are functioning at a low level of evolution at any moment, and how we rationalize our behaviour, deep inside we are aware of the harm we are causing, and that knowledge militates against our process of evolution. One might even see this as 'ourselves' at some level not giving 'ourselves' at a lower level permission to succeed. This is tantamount to our conscience holding us back, or in Freudian terms being impeded by our superego. Of course, the yogis don't have to postulate a morality coming from outside, as with the theory of the superego, because the atman and its surrounding anandamaya kosha are, according to yoga, already our centre and the font of all ethics and morality.

What can we do if those things are already there in our past? Simply realize them, divest them of any attached negative emotion such as fear or guilt, make amends where possible, then leave them there in the past and move forward in the present into a bright future.

There is no conflict as to the usefulness of the yamas and niyamas in our endeavour to evolve ourselves, but they are not always easy, especially at their deeper and more subtle levels. Sage Patanjali foresaw difficulties in our trying to follow them and recommended (as stated in *Four Chapters on Freedom*) the following: "When the mind gets disturbed by passions, one should practise pondering their opposites."

Swami Satyananda commented as follows:

During the practice of yamas and niyamas, the evil passions come up due to old habits, evil tendencies, etc., and they create disturbance. Suppression would not do. The best thing would be to ponder over the opposite tendencies. Thus hate is to be won over by love because they are the opposite of each other . . . For example, if one wants to be honest, one sometimes sees that dishonest people succeed in life, while honest people meet with failure. This may give rise to the evil thought that one should also be dishonest. This is . . . the wrong side of the argument. When this wrong side is advanced by the mind, it creates disturbance and may mislead the aspirant. In this situation, the opposite of dishonesty, i.e. honesty, should be cultivated through pondering over it . . . When it comes to mind that honesty does not pay and nobody cares for an honest man, one should be ready with the opposite argument, namely, that it is only through honesty that one can succeed on the spiritual path.

Karma yoga

When our life becomes action in the world, for the world, and for all the individuals that are in it, we tune into our higher self, whose substrata is 'us' instead of just 'me'. In this way we are becoming one with higher levels of the different aspects of ourselves, and evolving toward those levels. It sounds like a tall order, and it is. Most people need to be edging into sattwic levels to even contemplate it, but from there it accelerates our progress. However, people at all levels can be introduced to karma yoga and will benefit from practising it.

If actions are performed in tune with one's personal life direction and duty (*swadharma*), they become karma yoga and help us to evolve. Sri Krishna in the *Bhagavad Gita* was adamant about this. He said: "Better is one's own

284

duty, though devoid of merit, than the duty of another well discharged. Better is death in one's own duty (remember he was talking to a soldier – Arjuna); the duty of another is fraught with fear" (is productive of danger, by suppressing one's natural expression of personality).

It is not easy for most people to become aware of the 'right' path in life for them, but fortunately it is easier in many of our societies nowadays for us to follow our nature than it was in days gone by when people were trapped below the 'ceiling' of their social group and class.

Another important criterion of karma yoga is that the actions are done with meditative awareness – with full concentration and in the witness position. This allows us to observe every action and reaction of ourselves and the other people with whom we are interacting. It is a powerful learning experience, and one that allows us to grow.

Performing the actions without expectation of the rewards that come from the work, such as money, power, position, praise, etc., allows us to give full attention to the job, and to avoid disappointments that come when the desires are not fulfilled. This maintains us in a positive frame of mind.

Non-attachment to the rewards when they come is another way of avoiding entanglement in possessions, power, etc., which keeps us down in lower mind-states.

We try to perform our actions with a positive attitude, to see the situations in a favourable light. Remember Swami Niranjan's question: "When you see a rose, do you see the beautiful flower or the thorns? The choice is yours." This positive attitude also includes humour, and they both raise us in our life.

In the karma yoga lifestyle we try to work with peak efficiency. We can try to make it perfect, but remember this should not become an obsession with perfectionism – that is a loser; it should be more in the nature of a game.

Equanimity is another requirement of the karma yoga life, trying to keep balance of mind in positive or negative outcomes, in both success or failure (remember "failures are not stumbling blocks but stepping stones"), praise or criticism, fame or disgrace, etc.

An advanced form of karma yoga is where we can perform our activities without ego involvement – the sense that one is the non-doer – that the work 'does itself' and we are only the person who 'puts the pieces into place'. This becomes easier when we begin to recognize divine grace behind the work in which we are participating. At this point the work is being carried out at a much higher level of evolution than most people can imagine.

Ultimately, we can surrender all activities to the higher power. Then all actions become yoga. All life becomes a sacrament.

Bhakti yoga

Bhakti is the yoga of devotion. The practices we have mentioned until now have been appropriate for evolving the qualities of all the chakras. Bhakti yoga is especially loved by those people who are strong in anahata chakra, and it especially evolves anahata. Although bhakti is recommended for people who are more emotional and find the devotional path most compatible, it can also help to activate the anahata qualities for those people who are less emotional. For instance, people of a more intellectual or dynamic nature can often benefit greatly from the practices of bhakti. It can help them to remove emotional blockages that are not even touched in other ways.

In Chapter 14 we mentioned the recognized nine methods that are used to unfold bhakti, but it should be remembered that these are only steps that help a person to experience spontaneous devotion. In bhakti we are automatically experiencing the one-pointed concentration of raja yoga meditation, the service to humanity that we identify with karma yoga, and the realization of the highest consciousness that is the culmination of jnana yoga. So even though bhakti originally channels through devotion, love and compassion, it evolves the other qualities as well.

When we consider the security aspect of mooladhara chakra, we realize that oneness with the divine is the pinnacle of total security. Similarly, the experience of this oneness involves the bliss associated with swadhisthana chakra and the heights of communication associated with vishuddhi chakra. In the same way, when we serve humanity and the world, we are honing our ajna intellect and manipura skills of dynamic action, and are infused with the power to accomplish the best we can.

Jnana yoga

Jnana would seem to be the private domain of ajna chakra, and certainly the characteristics of the evolution of the aspects of ajna in us are those of the development of jnana yoga. However, jnana yoga has numerous influences on the other chakra systems. For instance, the intense self-enquiry that is its hallmark relates to all our qualities – security, joy, sexuality, power, self-esteem, love, communication, etc. The realizations we have, the life solutions we develop regarding these and the resulting overview that we get from jnana helps us to evolve the chakra systems.

Again this occurs when we apply the SWAN principle to these qualities within us. Identifying our *strengths* in any of the chakra qualities shows us the directions we can continue to pursue and augment. Realizing our *weaknesses* in any of them shows us the areas where we can work for improvement. Differentiating in any of the areas between what are our real *needs* and just our *wants* or *ambitions* gives us a clear direction where to pursue them, and where we are just wasting time (or worse). This of course is a part of the process of self-study (*swadhyaya*) from the niyamas of raja yoga.

Development of non-attachment (*vairagya*) applies to all the different qualities too, because any of them can entangle us and we can become addicted to their pleasures. In the same way, our development of right understanding (*viveka*) allows us to realize the traps in the lower levels of the personality aspects and to clearly differentiate between those and the realities of the more sattwic levels.

The awakening of intuition and wisdom at higher levels of jnana gives us insight into the higher levels of all the different chakra qualities, and allows us to stay at those higher levels more constantly, because our decisions and actions are right and don't lead to rajasic or tamasic outcomes.

Swara yoga – ida/pingala

When we deal with this important area, we immediately think about the activities of the two sides of the brain, and the ways they will channel the aspects of the chakra systems via the ten expressions of our personality. The stimulus for this activity of one side or the other is not just the flow of the *breath* through the nostrils, although that is crucially important. It is also the input of stimuli from any part of the *physical* body, from the flows of *vitality* and from the prevailing *mood* of the person. We can therefore use most of the yoga practices to boost one or other side, or (preferably) balance the two.

Most postures (*asanas*) have the balance inbuilt. For example, the flexibility practices (Pawanmuktasana 1) are perfectly balanced; everything we do on one side is repeated on the other. Salute to the sun (Surya Namaskara) is another balanced series and feeds stimuli equally into each of the sides. All forward and backward bending practices produce balance by acting centrally. All side bending practices feed in stimuli to both sides in a balanced way, as long as we are careful to do the counter postures equally. Similarly, all rotations are balanced, as long as we are careful to do the counter postures equally.

The cleansing practices (*shatkarmas*) are all well balanced, and the nasal cleansing (neti) practices are specific for balancing the swara long term.

Any breath practices (*pranayamas*) that alternate the nostrils such as alternate nostril breathing (nadi shodhana) will specifically balance the *swara*. Other pranayamas that use both nostrils simultaneously will maintain a balance that is already there.

The attitudes and locks (*mudras and bandhas*) maintain balance because, as they are performed centrally, they feed stimuli into both sides equally.

In the area of *mental relaxation and meditation*, shavasana and the sitting postures maintain the balance by their equal input of physical stimuli. Yoga Nidra is very specifically a practice of balancing ida and pingala because every point of body awareness that is performed on one side is repeated on the other side as well.

Functional M.R.I. experiments have shown that the prevailing mood of a person activates the appropriate side of the brain, and when the subject changes to an opposite mood, the activation moves over to the other side. The meditation practices balance a person's prevailing mood and therefore, presumably, reverse the effect that mood has on unbalancing the activity of the brain.

We can conclude that a balanced yoga class or personal sadhana such as those taught in the Satyananda Yoga system will help to balance the *swara*, even though we may not specifically try to do it in the session. This is an added bonus we receive, and our experience tells us that the balance can remain for some time after the class.

New vistas of knowledge

Yoga claims to be a way to evolve all dimensions of the individual, and it does just that. Its philosophy, techniques and lifestyle recommendations are simple and sensible. Its principles give us a clear model of the human personality on which to assess our present stage of evolution and the progress we make. And because of our individual evolvement and the improvement in the contribution we can make to our world, the prognosis for the future is improved.

So what does this all mean for ourselves as individuals and for the human community? Read the words of Swami Satyananda Saraswati in the conclusion.

Conclusion

In this book we have dealt with the personality aspect, but yoga is much more than that. It is a practical and extensive system of lifestyle, philosophy and techniques, which evolves *all* of the person's potentials, the physical, the vital, the mental, the emotional, the psychic and the spiritual qualities. Its roots lie many thousands of years ago, but it is so relevant for our present age that it is becoming deservedly popular worldwide nowadays. Through the ages, it developed from the experiences, meditations and realizations of wise people, and it gradually built into the vast body of knowledge it is today.

This short description of personality and its evolvement has given a yogic point of view about why we behave in the way we do. It has described many of the blockages that are keeping us back from realizing our highest potential, and it has laid before us a way to evolve all those dimensions of our personality. Maybe it has also gone some small way to giving us some understanding of each other, and helping a little to heal misunderstandings between individuals and groups of people.

Some of the explanations will have been familiar to Western psychiatrists and psychologists, but much of it will be new to them. However, taken together, these concepts describe a good model of personality, and one that has definite practical applications. What applications? The whole of the age-old science of yoga.

We will end with the following statement from Swami Satyananda Saraswati from *Dynamics of Yoga*.

We are living in an exciting age, an age of constant revolution in the human realm. The sciences have ushered in a technological era and civilization has reached its materialistic apex, with a great revolution in human thinking also. Freudian psychology, with its offshoot of the Neo-Freudian group, has demonstrated new dimensions of human personality. In biology, physics, chemistry, astrology, astronomy, ethics, philosophy and psychology, new vistas of knowledge have been opened up.

A mental revolution should match the technological revolution in the right perspective and in good faith. It is here that a need for resurrection of ancient values is keenly felt. While facts change, values remain constant. So what was fundamental to the concept of a good life and harmonious progress is still fundamental and not vitiated by changes in the social, political and economic spheres. Truth, beauty, and goodness are ideals which have received different interpretations, yet they endure as the ultimate pursuits of mankind.

Yoga, both in its philosophy and in its technique, is a means to the attainment of these ideals. Therefore, the paramount need of the day is to redeem yoga from oblivion and to restore it to its place of pride in the scheme of human knowledge.

The word yoga has been used, misused and abused . . . The confusion has been confounded by a piecemeal approach to yogic theory. The emphasis on asanas (necessary though they are) to the exclusion of the philosophy and metaphysics of yoga has in the long run reduced yoga to a method of body-building.

Man, to repeat a platitude, is a philosophical animal. In fact, he is the only animal who has a hunger and thirst for perfection. The history of mankind shows that at every stage we have been trying to perfect our social, political and religious institutions so that we can live a life free from all ills, devoted to the study and realization of the ultimate. Yoga philosophy is directed to this end, but its processes are prescribed at all levels of human personality. Yogic philosophy realizes that the body, as the abode of the soul, is as important as the mind; that physiology demands equal attention to psychology. Beginning with bodily discipline, the yoga system goes on to the transformation of the mental set-up by prescribing several different kinds of exertions of mind. It is only after integration between a sound body and vigorous mind that a sublime synthesis between the individual soul and the universal soul can be attained.

On the level of the body, no extra thought or expenditure of mental energy is required to demonstrate that good health can be kept up by good discipline. It is no self-abnegation to deny yourself that food which upsets your stomach. It is no sacrifice to desist from those delicacies which make one ill. At least blind self-interest should lead one to this sort of physical culture. The tragedy of all of us is that having attained a miraculous, self-sustaining body, we choose to take it for granted, and think that as long as it works smoothly, it is no part of our responsibility to maintain its machinery.

Depth psychology has shown that there is a form of psychic determinism which controls all our thoughts, actions and words. In fact, the revolution in modern psychological thought has infallibly led us to the conclusion that our conscious self is but a pygmy before the giant of our unconscious. The same truth was announced by the saints and seers of India as an intuitive truth, if not as a scientific maxim. The errors in man's personality go on multiplying in the process of living. Rectification of these errors can only be brought about if one addresses oneself to the task of understanding one's own mental structure.

It is here that the yogic system as enunciated by Sage Patanjali, despite the shifting interpretations it has been subjected to, comes as a helping guide. The Patanjali system is in absolute concord with the principles of depth psychology. Freud said that the unconscious is mud; but it is also to be realized that out of that mud blossoms a lotus flower. The elaborate structure of the human mind is definitely complicated, but by relentless honesty with oneself, where no quarter is given and none taken, one can see oneself as clearly, or more so, as one sees oneself in a mirror. The yogic disciplines for the mind essentially direct one towards this sort of realization.

Yogic philosophy offers no shortcuts to the ultimate; it prescribes a long and a tortuous way. The very brevity of our lives makes it imperative for us to understand the urgency of our mission. There is no realization distinct from the understanding of ourselves and there is no ignorance different from neglect of our being. Spiritual liberation dawns only when inner equipoise is attained by the rigours of the body and mind. And there cannot be any collective realization of divinity. Here each individual is left to himself.

Weakness of will, infirmity of decision, vacillations of mind may be equated with sin in puritan philosophy. They do not exist once the yogic discipline is imbibed in the self.

The plethora of spiritual movements has made spiritual choice difficult. Yoga is a heritage which comes to our rescue at a time when ambiguity surrounds philosophical thought. It is a heritage that needs to be preserved carefully and studied conscientiously in all its phases.

Yoga is available to all people, and is beneficial for all of us. It is really a practical science, and our personalities develop with its practice, so the real benefits come from experiencing yoga. Satyananda Yoga is a comprehensive, integral system which is available throughout the world, and people who are enthusiastically on the path of self-evolvement will benefit from learning it.

Glossary

Ahamkara – ego; awareness of the existence of 'I'

Ahimsa – non-violence

Ajapa japa – spontaneous repetition of mantra

Ajna chakra – psychic command centre situated in the midbrain; seat of intuition

Anahata chakra – psychic centre situated in the region of the heart and cardiac plexus; emotional centre

Anandamaya kosha – bliss body

Annamaya kosha – physical body

Antar mouna – inner silence; meditative technique involving thought observation

Apana – pranic air current operating in the lower abdominal region

Aparigraha – non-possessiveness

Asana – specific position of the body which channels prana and removes energy blocks

Asteya – honesty

Atma – divine spirit

AUM – universal cosmic mantra

Bandha – psycho-muscular energy lock

Bhagavad Gita – teachings of Sri Krishna to his disciple Arjuna

Bhakti yoga – yoga of channelling the intellect and emotions towards a higher purpose

Brahmacharya – continence; redirection of sexual energy towards spiritual and meditative experience

Bhramari pranayama – humming bee breath

Buddhi – intellectual mind; higher intelligence, discrimination

Chakra – major psychic centre in the subtle body responsible for specific physical and psychic functions

Chitta – memory; aspect of mind which receives impressions and stores them as samskaras

Chitta vritti – mental movement or modification

Dharana – concentration

Dharma – natural role one has to play in life; duty

Dhyana – meditation, total concentration

Drashta – witness, uninvolved observer

Dwesha – repulsion

Guna – attribute, quality or nature of the manifest world: tamas, rajas and sattwa

Hatha yoga – science of yoga which purifies the whole physical body

Ida nadi – pranic channel governing the mental processes

Ishwara pranidhana – cultivation of faith in a higher reality

Japa – mantra repetition

Jnana yoga – yoga of knowledge and wisdom

Jnanendriyas – five organs of sense perception and knowledge: ears, eyes, nose, tongue and skin

Kapalbhati pranayama – breathing practice to purify the frontal region of the brain

Karma yoga – yoga of action; action performed with meditative awareness

Karmendriyas – five organs of action: hands, feet, vocal cords, tongue, excretory and reproductive organs

Kosha – sheath or body; dimension of experience or existence

Krishna – guru of Arjuna in the Bhagavad Gita

Kunjal – regurgitative stomach cleansing

Laghoo shankhaprakshalana – intestinal cleansing

Maha prana – cosmic energy

Manas – instinctive mind; rational mind

Manipura chakra – psychic centre situated behind the navel, associated with vitality and energy

Manomaya kosha – mental body

Mantra – subtle sound vibration which liberates energy from the limitations of mundane awareness and expands the consciousness

Mooladhara chakra – lowest psychic centre in the human body from where kundalini shakti emerges; situated in the perineum in men and the cervix in women

Mudra – gesture or attitude utilized to express or channel pranic energy within the mind/body

Nadi –subtle pranic channel which conducts the flow of energy in the body

Neti – nasal cleansing

Niyamas – five inner disciplines; personal codes for self-improvement

Patanjali – sage who codified the Yoga Sutras; propounder of the eightfold system of raja yoga

Pawanmuktasana 1 – flexibility practices to loosen up the joints of the body

Pingala nadi – pranic channel conducting the vital energy

Prana – vital air or energy force, sustaining life and creation

Pranayama – breathing practices to control and expand the range of vital energy

Pranamaya kosha – energy/vitality body

Pratyahara – process of withdrawing the senses from external objects

Raga – attraction

Raja yoga – eightfold path classified by Sage Patanjali in the Yoga Sutras

Rajas – guna representing the dynamic, active state of mind and nature

Sahasrara – spiritual centre situated at crown of head; represents state of enlightenment

Samadhi – transcendental consciousness
Samana – pranic air current located in the middle region of the body
Samskara – unconscious memory or impression which sets up impulses and trains of thought
Sankalpa – resolve; positive affirmation
Satsang – gathering of spiritually minded people in which the ideals and principles of truth are discussed
Sattwa – guna representing steadiness, purity and harmony, experienced when tamas and rajas are balanced
Satya – absolute truth; reality
Shankhaprakshalana – intestinal cleansing
Shatkarmas – cleansing techniques of hatha yoga
Shaucha – cleanliness, internal and external
So-Ham – psychic sound and mantra of the breath
Surya namaskara – salute to the sun; series of twelve postures which have a vitalizing effect on the energy
Sushumna nadi – main nadi in the centre of the spinal cord
Sutra – verse
Swadhyaya – self-study, self-enquiry
Swadharma – right individual path
Swadhisthana chakra – psychic centre situated at the base of the spinal column, associated with the sacral plexus; storehouse of subconscious impressions
Swara yoga – yoga concerned with pranic rhythms and their control through the breath
Tamas – guna responsible for inertia, laziness, procrastination and fear of change
Tapas – austerity; effort involving purification and self-discipline
Udana – pranic air current in the area of the nose and face
Ujjayi pranayama – psychic breath
Vairagya – non-attachment; state in which one remains internally calm and balanced under all circumstances
Vasanas – deep-rooted desire in the unconscious mind
Vijnanamaya kosha – higher mental body
Vikshepa – oscillation of mind

Vishuddhi chakra – psychic centre located at the level of the throat pit or the thyroid gland, connected with communication

Viveka – power to discriminate correctly; right knowledge or understanding

Vritti – mental fluctuation or pattern

Vyana – pranic air current pervading the whole body

Yamas – five self-restraints or rules of conduct

Yoga – methods and practices leading to a state of union between individual and universal awareness

Yoga Sutras – classical yoga text codified by Sage Patanjali, which delineates the eight-fold path of raja yoga

Bibliography

Swami Satyananda Saraswati, *Asana Pranayama Mudra Bandha*, 3rd revised edn, Yoga Publications Trust, Munger, Bihar, 2002.

Swami Satyananda Saraswati, *Dynamics of Yoga: The Foundations of Bihar Yoga*, 2nd edn, Yoga Publications Trust, Munger, Bihar, 2002.

Swami Satyananda Saraswati, *Four Chapters on Freedom: Commentary on the Yoga Sutras of Patanjali*, Yoga Publications Trust, Munger, Bihar, 2000.

Swami Satyananda Saraswati, *Kundalini Tantra*, Yoga Publications Trust, Munger, Bihar, 2002.

Swami Satyananda Saraswati, *Meditations from the Tantras*, 2nd edn, Yoga Publications Trust, Munger, Bihar, 2000.

Swami Satyananda Saraswati, *A Systematic Course in the Ancient Tantric Techniques of Yoga and Kriya*, Yoga Publications Trust, Munger, Bihar, 2003.

Swami Satyananda Saraswati, *Yoga Nidra*, 6th edn, Yoga Publications Trust, Munger, Bihar, 2001.

Swami Niranjanananda Saraswati, *Yoga Darshan: Vision of the Yoga Upanishads*, Yoga Publications Trust, Munger, Bihar, 2002.

Swami Sivananda Saraswati, *The Bhagavad Gita*, 10th edn, The Divine Life Trust Society, Rishikesh, 1995.

Swami Chinmayananda, *Holy Geeta*, Central Chinmaya Mission Trust, Bombay, 1995.

References

Chapter 2

[1] Easwaran, E., *The Compassionate Universe*, Penguin, New Delhi, 1989.

Chapter 5

[1] Joseph R., 'The Right Cerebral Hemisphere: Emotion, Music, Visual-spatial Skills, Body Image, Dreams and Awareness', *J Clin Psychol*, 1988, Sept 44 (5), pp 630–73.

[2] Gazzaniga, M., *Science News*, 1996, Feb 24.

[3] Schiffer F., Zaidel E., Bogen J., Chasan-Taber S., 'Different Psychological Status in the Two Hemispheres of Two Split-brain Patients', *Neuropsychiatry Neuropsychol Behav Neurol*, 1998, July 11 (3), pp 151–6.

[4] Duda P.D., Brown J., 'Lateral Asymmetry of Positive and Negative Emotions', *Cortex*, 1984, June 20 (2), pp 253–61.

[5] McLaren J., Bryson S.E., 'Hemispheric Asymmetries in the Perception of Emotional and Neutral Faces', *Cortex*, 1987, Dec 23 (4), pp 645–54.

[6] Davidson R.J., Chapman J.P., Chapman L.J., Henriques J.B., 'Asymmetrical Brain Electrical Activity Discriminates Between Psychometrically-matched Verbal and Spatial Cognitive Tasks', *Psychophysiology*, 1990, Sept 27 (5), pp 528–43.

[7] Klein R., Pilon D., Prosser S., Shannahoff-Khalsa D., 'Nasal Airflow Asymmetries and Human Performance', *Biol Psychol*, 1986, Oct 23 (2), pp 127–37.

[8] Levick S.E., Lorig T., Wexler B.E., Gur R.E., Gur R.C., Schwartz G.E., 'Asymmetrical Visual Deprivation: A Technique to Differentially Influence Lateral Hemispheric Function', *Percept Mot Skills*, 1993, June 76 (3 Pt 2), pp 1363–82.

[9] Shannahoff-Khalsa D., 'The Ultradian Rhythm of Alternating Cerebral Hemispheric Activity', *Int J Neurosci*, 1993, June 70 (3–4), pp 285–98.

[10] Shannahoff-Khalsa D., 'The Effects of Unilateral Forced Nostril Breathing on Cognition', *Int J Neurosci*, 1991, Apr 57 (3–4), pp 239–49.

Chapter 6
[1] Hilgard, E.R., Atkinson, R.C. & Atkinson, R.L., *Introduction to Psychology*, Harcourt Brace Jovanovich, New York, 1979.

[2] Bach, R., *Illusions*, Dell Publishing Co., New York, 1977.

Chapter 11
[1] Ornish, D., *Reversing Heart Disease*, Ballantine Books, New York, 1992.

[2] *New Scientist*, 27 November 1999, 14 October 2000, 25 August 2001, 19 December 2001, 26 July 2002, 9 January 2003.

See also: Doll, R., 'The Benefit of Alcohol in Moderation', *Drug Alcohol Rev*, 1998, 17: pp 353–363, and *Medical Journal of Australia*, 7 August 2000.

[3] Eron, L.D., 'Does Television Cause Aggression?' in Hilgard, E.R., Atkinson, R.L. & Atkinson, R.C., *Introduction to Psychology*, Harcourt Brace Jovanovich, New York, 1979.

Chapter 17
[1] For a full explanation see the article 'Overcoming the Tyranny of Memory' by Dr Rishi Vivekananda, in *YOGA* magazine, November-December 2003, published by Sivananda Math, Munger, Bihar.

Index

Notes